YEAR 5

Key Lessons in Numeracy

# Numbers and the Number System

Paul Broadbent

Kathryn Church

Heinemann Educational Publishers
Halley Court, Jordan Hill, Oxford, OX2 8EJ
a division of Reed Educational and Professional Publishing Ltd

Heinemann is a registered trademark of Reed Educational and Professional Publishing Ltd

Oxford   Melbourne   Auckland
Johannesburg   Blantyre   Gaborone
Ibadan   Portsmouth (NH)   Chicago

© Paul Broadbent and Kathryn Church 1999

Acknowledgements

The publisher would like to thank the DfEE for permission to quote from the National Numeracy Strategy *Framework for teaching mathematics*.

First published 1999

04   03   02   01   00   99
10  9  8  7  6  5  4  3  2  1


Individual                      ISBN 0 435 02534 1
Key Stage 2 Omnibus Pack   ISBN 0 435 02545 7
Complete Omnibus Pack      ISBN 0 435 02550 3


Designed by Susan Clarke
Illustrated by Jan Lewis
Cover design by Tinstar
Printed and bound in Great Britain

# Contents

# Introduction

### The National Numeracy Strategy

**Key Lessons in Numeracy** is a series of books written to support teachers implementing the National Numeracy Strategy. *Numbers and the Number System Year 3* focuses on the 'Numbers and the Number System' strand of the National Numeracy Strategy 'Framework'. It provides a bank of 20 lessons for year 3 which each deal with key teaching objectives, including those that introduce mathematical content that may be 'new' to year 3 classes, but also giving support for topics that are known to be difficult to teach.

Each lesson aims to give teachers everything needed for a well structured, purposeful and successful lesson. In line with the recommendations of the National Numeracy Strategy, the lessons in *Numbers and the Number System Year 3* provide:

- support for direct teaching
- an emphasis on mental methods of calculation
- interactive involvement with the pupils through careful questioning
- lessons which are well paced and offer challenge
- a variety of activities to consolidate and extend understanding.

### Resources

A range of resources will be useful as part of the interactive teaching approach promoted within *Numbers and the Number System Year 3*:

**'Show me' activities** involve pupils showing the answer by holding up a prop such as a digit card or fan number. In this way all pupils are involved and the teacher has a clear idea of their responses and understanding. This method also avoids individuals being singled out to respond orally. Resource sheets 1 (fan numbers) and 2 (digit cards), provided at the end of the book, can be photocopied for use with appropriate lessons.

The **counting stick** (a rule marked into 10 equal sections) is also referred to regularly as a teaching aid.

*fan numbers*

*digit cards*

*counting stick*

## Using this book

The National Numeracy Strategy recommends that each numeracy lesson should start with a 5–10 minute mental maths warm-up. A range of commercially produced resources are available from which you can choose activities for this section of the lesson. The focus within *Numbers and the Number System Year 3* is support for the main teaching session and pupil activities.

When planning teaching objectives on a medium-term or weekly basis the Numeracy 'Framework' should be the starting point. Once the teaching objectives have been chosen, the table on pp. 8–9 can be used to choose the appropriate lesson and topic. The intention within *Numbers and the Number System Year 3* is not to provide comprehensive coverage of the year 3 curriculum within a mere 20 lessons – that would clearly be impossible. Rather, it is to provide a starting point for teaching the most important aspects of the Numbers and the Number System strand of the 'Framework'. A range of consolidation – both teaching and activity – will be needed, depending on the needs of individual classes and children.

A typical lesson plan is shown on p. 7, with the main sections labelled. The structure of each lesson follows a broadly similar format: a step-by-step description of the teching followed by 3 photocopiable activities geared towards the needs of different ability groups. For each lesson, **Further activities** provide suggestions for follow-up work related to the topic.

*lesson title*

*resources to prepare and organize before the lesson*

*outline of pupil activity aimed at the majority of the class*

*outline of pupil activiy aimed at higher attainers, or for an extension lesson*

*specific lesson objective*

*previous stage of learning before this objective is taught*

## Counting and properties of numbers

**LESSON 1** — **Counting objects by grouping**

**Lesson objective**

- to count larger collections by grouping them, for example, in tens then other numbers

**Resources**

- collections of more than 40 different objects (such as cubes, conkers, buttons, pencils), about 100 penny coins, **PCM1a, 1b, 1c**

**Language**

- grouping, total, count

**Prior learning**

- counting smaller collections in twos, fives and tens
- counting in multiples of 2, 5 and 10

**Teaching** — *whole class: about 15 minutes*

- Explain to the children that this lesson is about using quick and reliable ways to count large collections of objects.
- Ask the children to stand in two lines next to each other. Count them one by one, starting with the first child in each line, then the next one in each line, and so on.
  *Can anyone think of a quicker way?*
  (If the suggestion to count in twos is not forthcoming, suggest it yourself.)
- Ask one of the children to demonstrate how to count the children in twos, then ask the class to sit down. (You might like to start the counting off if there is any confusion.)
  *What else could we count in twos?*
  Try out some of the suggestions the children offer, counting together in twos. To start them off you might, perhaps, like to draw attention to Noah and how he counted the animals.
- *How could we count the total number of right-hand fingers and thumbs in the class?*
  Ask the class to hold up their right hand and count them in fives together.
  *What else could we count in fives?*
  Try out some of the suggestions, counting together in fives. A couple of examples might include counting coins or counting groups of children at each table, and so on.
- *Could we count anything in tens?*
  Try out some of the children's suggestions, counting together in tens. You might like to start off with fingers, toes or coins.
- Explain that large collections of objects are often counted in twos, fives or tens for speed and simplicity. Demonstrate this by: putting a handful of counters on the desk and counting them into a container in twos; providing some cubes, asking a few children to take 5 each, and then counting in fives together as a class as the handfuls of cubes are dropped in a container; putting about 35 penny pieces in piles of 10 and counting the total in tens together, making the point that any extras are counted after the complete piles of 10.

**Activities** — *about 15 minutes*

**Core** (for whole class or average attainers)

Provide five large collections of objects for each table, with a range of numbers of objects from 20 to 60, for example, 20 buttons, 35 shells, 42 counters, 50 crayons and 58 cubes.

Explain to the children that they will be practising counting the collections of objects by grouping them. Hand out copies of **PCM1a** for the children to record their answers and the counting method used. Encourage the children to try different methods. For the second half of the activity, point to the pictures and explain that they have to find the total number in each set by ringing groups in twos, fives or tens.

**Extension** (for extension lesson or higher attainers)

Give the children **PCM1b**. Tell them that they will be taking handfuls of mixed coins and finding how many of each coin there are by grouping them. They then work out how many coins in total there were in each handful. Make sure they understand they are not totalling the value of the coins.

**Support** (for reinforcement lesson or lower attainers)

Work with this group as they practise counting sets of objects. Hand out **PCM1c** for record-keeping. Use different groups of objects, such as interlocking cubes and 1p coins, as well as the children themselves, and ask individual children how they would count the number of things in each set. Complete a few counts orally, making sure they understand how to record their results on the **PCM** by ticking the column to show the grouping used, then leave them to work in pairs or individually to finish the task. If necessary, restrict them to counting in twos and tens.

**Plenary** — *whole class: about 10 minutes*

Focusing on the second part of the 'Core' activity, ask the children working on it how many things there were in each collection and how they grouped them. Compare their results and encourage them to offer reasons for any differences.

Discuss with the children how collections of money are counted, for example, the money collected in school for a trip or a book club. Explain that usually 1p pieces are grouped in tens, 2p pieces in fives, 5p pieces in twos or tens, and so on, and then the total is counted.

Establish that grouping saves time and is more reliable than counting in ones as you are less likely to lose count. Also, checking is easier when objects are placed in groups.

Ask them to try to use this next time they have to count a large number of objects.

**Further activities**

- At an assembly, ask the class to suggest a method for finding the total number of children in the hall by grouping in some way. Depending on the responses, it may be necessary to observe the seating arrangements. If it is not too disruptive, the class might ask the children to stand up and then count the groups of 2, 5 or 10 as they sit down.
- This activity could be extended to investigate the possible maximum 'people capacity' of the hall.

## Match to Numeracy Framework

**Year 3 teaching programme**
**Numbers and the number system**

| | lesson | lesson objectives |
|---|---|---|
| **Counting, properties of numbers and number sequences** | | |
| • Count larger collections by grouping them: for example, in tens, then other numbers. | 1 | to count larger collections by grouping them, for example, in tens then other numbers |
| • Describe and extend number sequences: **count on or back in tens or hundreds, starting from any two- or three-digit number.** | 2 | to count on or back in tens or hundreds, starting from any 2-digit or 3-digit number |
| count on or back in twos starting from any two-digit number, and recognize odd and even numbers to at least 100; | 3 | to count on or back in twos, starting from any 2-digit number, and recognize odd and even numbers to at least 100 |
| count on in steps of 3, 4 or 5 from any small number to at least 50, then back again. | 4 | count on in steps of 3, 4 or 5 from any small number to at least 50, then back again |
| • Recognise two-digit and three-digit multiples of 2, 5 or 10, and three-digit multiples of 50 and 100. | 5 | to recognize 2-digit multiples of 2, 5 and 10 |
| | 6 | to recognize 3-digit multiples of 2, 5, 10, 50 and 100 |
| **Place value and ordering** | | |
| • **Read and write whole numbers to at least 1000** in figures and words. | 7 | to read and write whole numbers to at least 1000 in figures and words |
| • **Know what each digit represents,** and partition three-digit numbers into a multiple of 100, a multiple of tens and ones (HTU) | 8. | to know what each digit in a 3-digit number represents (HTU) |
| | 9 | to partition 3-digit numbers into a multiple of 100, a multiple of 10 and units (HTU) |
| • Read and begin to write the vocabulary of comparing and ordering numbers, including ordinal numbers to at least 100. Compare two given three-digit numbers, say which is more or less, and give a number which lies between them. | 10 | to compare any two 3-digit numbers, say which is more or less, and give a number which lies between them |
| | 13 | to order amounts of money involving pounds and multiples of ten pence, using appropriate vocabulary |
| • Say the number that is 1, 10 or 100 more or less than any given two- or three-digit number. | 11 | to say the number that is 1, 10 or 100 more or less than any given 2- or 3-digit number |
| • **Order whole numbers to at least 1000,** and position them on a number line. | 12 | to order whole numbers to at least 1000, and position them on a number line |
| **Estimating and rounding** | | |
| • Read and begin to write the vocabulary of estimation and approximation. Give a sensible estimate up to about 100 objects. | 14 | to read and begin to write the vocabulary of estimation and approximation, and to give a sensible estimate of up to 100 objects |
| • Round any two-digit number to the nearest 10 and any three-digit number to the nearest 100. | 15 | to round any 2-digit number to the nearest 10 and any 3-digit number to the nearest 100 |

## Year 3 teaching programme
## Numbers and the number system

| | lesson | lesson objectives |
|---|---|---|
| **Fractions** | | |
| • **Recognise unit fractions such as $\frac{1}{2}, \frac{1}{3}, \frac{1}{4}, \frac{1}{5}, \frac{1}{10}$ ... and use them to find fractions of shapes and numbers.** | 16 | to recognise unit fractions such as $\frac{1}{2}, \frac{1}{3}, \frac{1}{4}, \frac{1}{5}, \frac{1}{10}$, and use them to find fractions of shapes |
| | 17 | to recognise and name fractions such as $\frac{1}{2}, \frac{1}{3}, \frac{1}{4}, \frac{1}{5}, \frac{1}{10}$, and use them to find fractions of numbers |
| Begin to recognize simple fractions that are several parts of a whole, such as $\frac{3}{4}, \frac{2}{3}$ or $\frac{3}{10}$. | 18 | to recognize simple fractions that are several parts of a whole, such as $\frac{3}{4}, \frac{2}{3}$ or $\frac{3}{10}$ |
| Begin to recognize simple equivalent fractions: for example, five tenths and one half, five fifths and one whole. | 19 | to recognize simple equivalent fractions |
| Compare familiar fractions: for example, know that on the number line one half lies between one quarter and three quarters. | 20 | to compare familiar fractions |
| Estimate a simple fraction. | | |

# Counting and properties of numbers

**LESSON 1**     **Counting objects by grouping**

## Lesson objective

- to count larger collections by grouping them, for example, in tens then other numbers

## Language

- grouping, total, count

## Resources

- collections of more than 40 different objects (such as cubes, conkers, buttons, pencils), about 100 penny coins, **PCM1a, 1b, 1c**

## Prior learning

- counting smaller collections in twos, fives and tens
- counting in multiples of 2, 5 and 10

---

**Teaching**     *whole class: about 15 minutes*

- Explain to the children that this lesson is about using quick and reliable ways to count large collections of objects.

- Ask the children to stand in two lines next to each other. Count them one by one, starting with the first child in each line, then the next one in each line, and so on.
  *Can anyone think of a quicker way?*
  (If the suggestion to count in twos is not forthcoming, suggest it yourself.)

- Ask one of the children to demonstrate how to count the children in twos, then ask the class to sit down. (You might like to start the counting off if there is any confusion.)
  *What else could we count in twos?*
  Try out some of the suggestions the children offer, counting together in twos. To start them off you might, perhaps, like to draw attention to Noah and how he counted the animals.

- *How could we count the total number of right-hand fingers and thumbs in the class?*
  Ask the class to hold up their right hand and count them in fives together.
  *What else could we count in fives?*
  Try out some of the suggestions, counting together in fives. A couple of examples might include counting coins or counting groups of children at each table, and so on.

- *Could we count anything in tens?*
  Try out some of the children's suggestions, counting together in tens. You might like to start off with fingers, toes or coins.

- Explain that large collections of objects are often counted in twos, fives or tens for speed and simplicity. Demonstrate this by: putting a handful of counters on the desk and counting them into a container in twos; providing some cubes, asking a few children to take 5 each, and then counting in fives together as a class as the handfuls of cubes are dropped in a container; putting about 35 penny pieces in piles of 10 and counting the total in tens together, making the point that any extras are counted after the complete piles of 10.

**Core** (for whole class or average attainers)

Provide five large collections of objects for each table, with a range of numbers of objects from 20 to 60, for example, 20 buttons, 35 shells, 42 counters, 50 crayons and 58 cubes.

Explain to the children that they will be practising counting the collections of objects by grouping them. Hand out copies of **PCM1a** for the children to record their answers and the counting method used. Encourage the children to try different methods. For the second half of the activity, point to the pictures and explain that they have to find the total number in each set by ringing groups in twos, fives or tens.

**Extension** (for extension lesson or higher attainers)

Give the children **PCM1b**. Tell them that they will be taking handfuls of mixed coins and finding how many of each coin there are by grouping them. They then work out how many coins in total there were in each handful. Make sure they understand they are not totalling the value of the coins.

**Support** (for reinforcement lesson or lower attainers)

Work with this group as they practise counting sets of objects. Hand out **PCM1c** for record-keeping. Use different groups of objects, such as interlocking cubes and 1p coins, as well as the children themselves, and ask individual children how they would count the number of things in each set. Complete a few counts orally, making sure they understand how to record their results on the **PCM** by ticking the column to show the grouping used, then leave them to work in pairs or individually to finish the task. If necessary, restrict them to counting in twos and tens.

**Plenary**  *whole class: about 10 minutes*

Focusing on the second part of the 'Core' activity, ask the children working on it how many things there were in each collection and how they grouped them. Compare their results and encourage them to offer reasons for any differences.

Discuss with the children how collections of money are counted, for example, the money collected in school for a trip or a book club. Explain that usually 1p pieces are grouped in tens, 2p pieces in fives, 5p pieces in twos or tens, and so on, and then the total is counted.

Establish that grouping saves time and is more reliable than counting in ones as you are less likely to lose count. Also, checking is easier when objects are placed in groups.

Ask them to try to use this next time they have to count a large number of objects.

**Further activities**

- At an assembly, ask the class to suggest a method for finding the total number of children in the hall by grouping in some way. Depending on the responses, it may be necessary to observe the seating arrangements. If it is not too disruptive, the class might ask the children to stand up and then count the groups of 2, 5 or 10 as they sit down.

- This activity could be extended to investigate the possible maximum 'people capacity' of the hall.

## Counting objects by grouping

Count how many objects there are in each group.

Record your results in the table.

What method did you use?

| Collection | Total | Counting method |
|---|---|---|
| 1 | | |
| 2 | | |
| 3 | | |
| 4 | | |
| 5 | | |

Now find how many objects there are.
Circle the groups to show your counting method.

Total: [ ]

Total: [ ]

Total: [ ]

Total: [ ]

Name: ...................................................................................................

# Counting objects by grouping

You need: a pile of 1p, 2p, 5p and 10p coins, all mixed up

- Take a handful of coins.
- Group the coins by value. Count how many of each coin you have.
- Now take another handful and repeat.

| Coins | Total |
|-------|-------|
| 1p | |
| 2p | |
| 5p | |
| 10p | |

Total: [    ]

| Coins | Total |
|-------|-------|
| 1p | |
| 2p | |
| 5p | |
| 10p | |

Total: [    ]

- - - - - - - - - - - - - - - - - - - - - - - - - - - - - - - - - - - - - - - - - ✂

Name: ...................................................................................................

# Counting objects by grouping

Write the name of the collection you are counting.
Count the objects and tick how you counted them.

| Collection | Total | Counting in: | | |
|------------|-------|------|-------|------|
| | | twos | fives | tens |
| | | | | |

**Counting on and back**

### Lesson objective

● to count on or back in tens or hundreds, starting from any 2-digit or 3-digit number

### Language

● count on, count back, count backwards, count forwards, 2-digit, 3-digit

### Resources

● class number line (Resource sheet 6), class 1–100 square (Resource sheet 5), abacus, **PCM2a, 2b, 2c**

### Prior learning

● counting in units, tens and hundreds from 2-digit numbers

---

**Teaching**     *whole class: about 15 minutes*

● Explain to the children that this lesson is about counting forwards and backwards in units, tens and hundreds, from different 2-digit and 3-digit numbers.

● With reference to the number line and 1–100 square, if necessary, ask the class to:

*Start at 45 and count on 6 to 51. Start at 63 and count back 5. Start at 97 and count on 8. Start at 104 and count back 7. Start at 296 and count on 6 then back.*

● *Start at 20 and count on in tens to 80. Start at 35 and count on in tens to 95 and back. Start at 70 and count on in tens to 130. Start at 140 and count back in tens to 70. Start at 88 and count on in tens to 148 and back.*

● *Start at 0 and count in hundreds to 600 and back to 0. Start at 6 and count in hundreds to 806.*

● Show the children the abacus and explain how it represents numbers in units, tens and hundreds, and that one bead represents one digit. Demonstrate how it works for different numbers written on the board, then ask different children to show particular numbers on the abacus.

Use the abacus to help the children in counts such as the following:

*Count in ones, starting from 50, forwards to 65 and back to 50.*

*Count in ones, starting from 95, forwards to 115 and back to 95.*

*Count in ones, starting from 190, forwards to 210 and back to 190.*

*Count in tens, starting from 0, forwards to 60 and back to 0.*

*Count in tens, starting from 80, forwards to 150 and back to 80.*

*Count in tens, starting from 13, forwards to 73 and back to 13.*

*Count in tens, starting from 167, forwards to 227 and back to 167.*

*Count in hundreds, starting from 0, forwards to 1000 and back to 0.*

*Count in hundreds, starting from 69, forwards to 569 and back to 69.*

*Count in hundreds, starting from 7, forwards to 607 and back to 7.*

*Count in hundreds, starting from 264, forwards to 864 and back to 264.*

Now encourage the children to try similar counts, but this time without the abacus.

*about 15 minutes*

### Core (for whole class or average attainers)

Give out **PCM2a**, pointing out that there are two parts. In the first part of the activity the children need to continue the sequences, counting in ones, tens or hundreds. The second part involves colouring in the squares in a sequence (counting in tens) to get through each maze.

### Extension (for extension lesson or higher attainers)

Hand out **PCM2b**. Explain to the children that they will be completing counting sequences and explaining how the sequences work before making up their own sequences counting in tens and hundreds.

### Support (for reinforcement lesson or lower attainers)

Continue to work with this group. Practise a few oral counts with them similar to those at the beginning of the lesson using the number line, 1–100 square or abacus. Give them **PCM2c** and stay with the children as the first number line sequence is completed.

**Plenary** *whole class: about 10 minutes*

Ask the children to:
*Count on 7 from 154.*
*Count back 8 from 243.*
*Count on 5 tens from 38.*
*Count back 6 tens from 527.*
*Count on 4 hundreds from 19.*
*Count back 7 hundreds from 705.*

Write some sequences on the board such as these:

___ 48 58 68 ___     ___ 147 148 149 ___     ___ 380 480 580 ___

Ask different children to fill in the missing numbers.

Remind them that an abacus can help to count on or back.

### Further activities

● Play 'All change'. As a class, count in ones starting from any 2-digit number, using rhythm counting such as 'thigh, clap, snap, snap' (slap thighs, clap hands, snap the fingers of the left hand with the count, snap the fingers of the right hand with the count). After about ten numbers, change the step to 10, by saying: 'Change to tens' without altering the rhythm. So:

● Extend this activity by counting backwards in ones, tens and hundreds.

| thigh | clap | snap | snap | thigh | clap | snap | snap | thigh | clap | snap | snap |
|-------|------|------|------|-------|------|------|------|-------|------|------|------|
|       |      | 15   | 16   |       |      | 17   | 18   | Change |     | to   | tens |

| thigh | clap | snap | snap | thigh | clap | snap | snap | thigh | clap | snap | snap |
|-------|------|------|------|-------|------|------|------|-------|------|------|------|
|       |      | 28   | 38   |       |      | 48   | 58   |       |      | 68   | 78   |

Then change the step to 100:

| thigh | clap | snap | snap | thigh | clap | snap | snap | thigh | clap | snap | snap |
|-------|------|------|------|-------|------|------|------|-------|------|------|------|
| Change |     | to   | hundreds |   |      | 178  | 278  |       |      | 378  | 478  |

Name: ...............................................................................................

## Counting on and back

Continue these number sequences.

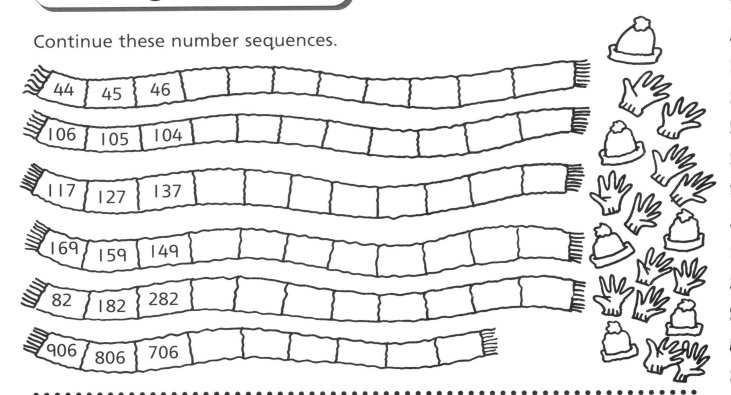

Scarf 1: 44 | 45 | 46 | | | | | | |
Scarf 2: 106 | 105 | 104 | | | | | | |
Scarf 3: 117 | 127 | 137 | | | | | | |
Scarf 4: 169 | 159 | 149 | | | | | | |
Scarf 5: 82 | 182 | 282 | | | | | | |
Scarf 6: 906 | 806 | 706 | | | | | |

Now follow the number pattern to find your way out of the mazes.

**Start** ▼

| 48 | 58 | 59 | 64 | 74 | 86 | 102 |
|-----|-----|-----|-----|-----|-----|-----|
| 49 | 68 | 78 | 88 | 89 | 99 | 112 |
| 57 | 74 | 84 | 98 | 108 | 118 | 128 |
| 218 | 208 | 198 | 99 | 158 | 148 | 138 |
| 228 | 229 | 188 | 178 | 168 | 169 | 150 |
| 238 | 254 | 189 | 176 | 150 | 170 | 151 |
| 248 | 258 | 268 | 248 | 254 | 308 | 216 |
| 278 | 218 | 278 | 288 | 298 | 299 | 317 |
| 279 | 219 | 267 | 287 | 308 | 318 | 328 |

▼ Finish

**Start** ▼

| 104 | 114 | 124 | 130 | 155 | 165 | 175 |
|-----|-----|-----|-----|-----|-----|-----|
| 110 | 135 | 134 | 144 | 154 | 164 | 170 |
| 111 | 215 | 210 | 145 | 135 | 174 | 118 |
| 115 | 216 | 214 | 204 | 194 | 184 | 185 |
| 244 | 234 | 224 | 225 | 195 | 180 | 181 |
| 254 | 256 | 258 | 350 | 354 | 364 | 374 |
| 264 | 274 | 284 | 343 | 344 | 368 | 384 |
| 265 | 272 | 294 | 295 | 334 | 335 | 394 |
| 300 | 303 | 304 | 314 | 324 | 325 | 404 |

▼ Finish

**Key Lessons in Numeracy:**
Numbers and the Number System Year 3

© P. Broadbent and K.Church 1999. Heinemann Educational Ltd.
For copyright restrictions, see reverse of title page.

Name: ........................................................................................................  **2b**

## Counting on and back

Copy and complete these number sequences.
Write a sentence to explain how you worked them out.

1. <u>78</u>   <u>88</u>   ____   ____   ____   <u>128</u>   ____   ____

    _____

2. ____   ____   <u>347</u>   <u>447</u>   ____   ____   <u>747</u>   ____

    _____

3. ____   <u>669</u>   <u>679</u>   ____   <u>699</u>   ____   ____   ____

Now make up five more sequences of your own, counting in tens and hundreds.

    _____

4. <u>846</u>   <u>836</u>   <u>826</u>   ____   ____   ____   ____   ____

    _____

- - - - - - - - - - - - - - - - - - - - - - - - - - - - - - - - - - - - - - - - - - ✂

Name: ........................................................................................................ **2c**

## Counting on and back

Continue the patterns on these number lines.
Write the numbers that the bee lands on.

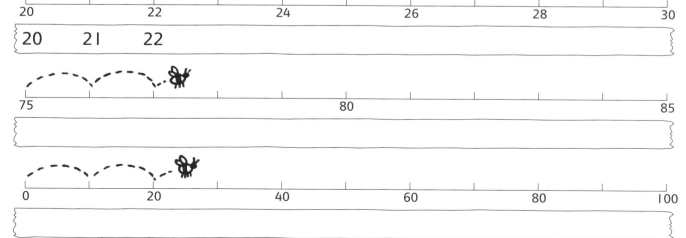

**Key Lessons in Numeracy:**
Numbers and the Number System Year 3

© P. Broadbent and K.Church 1999. Heinemann Educational Ltd.
For copyright restrictions, see reverse of title page.

**Odd and even numbers**

## Lesson objective

● to count on or back in twos, starting from any 2-digit number, and recognize odd and even numbers to at least 100

## Language

● odd, even, sum, multiples of 2, sequence, rule

## Resources

● class number line (Resource sheet 6), fan numbers or digit cards (Resource sheets 1 and 2), class 1–100 square (Resource sheet 3), **PCM3a, 3b, 3c**

## Prior learning

● recognizing odd and even numbers to 30
● counting in twos
● using Venn diagrams

### Teaching    *whole class: about 15 minutes*

● Explain to the children that this lesson is about learning the rules concerning odd and even numbers.

● With reference to the number line, if necessary, ask the class to count in twos to 30 starting at 0.
*What do we call all the numbers which are multiples of 2?*

Now count in twos to 29 starting at 1.
*What do we call all those numbers?*

Count in twos from 30 to 50 and back to 30.
*Are they even numbers or odd numbers? How do you know?*

Count in twos from 29 to 51 and back to 29.
*Are they even numbers or odd numbers? How do you know?*

Count in twos from 50 to 100.
*Are they even numbers or odd numbers? How do you know? What is the rule for recognizing an even number?*

Make sure the children realize that even numbers divide exactly by 2 and have a units digit of 0, 2, 4, 6, or 8.

Count in twos from 51 to 99.
*Are they even numbers or odd numbers? How do you know? What is the rule for recognizing an odd number?*

Make sure the children realize that odd numbers have 1 left over when divided by 2 and have a units digit of 1, 3, 5, 7 or 9.

● Ask the children to use their fan numbers or digit cards to show: an odd number; an even number; an odd number between 81 and 87; an even number between 68 and 74; an odd number greater than 50; an even number greater than 60, and so on.

### Activities    *about 15 minutes*

**Core** (for whole class or average attainers)

Give the children **PCM3a**, telling them that they will be continuing number sequences, sorting numbers into 'odd' and 'even' sets, then adding some numbers together to see whether the total is odd or even.

**Extension** (for extension lesson or higher attainers)

Tell the children that they will be finding rules for checking the sum of odd and even numbers. Hand out **PCM3b** for them to complete.

**Support** (for reinforcement lesson or lower attainers)

Give the children **PCM3c** and explain that they will be looking at the pattern of odd and even numbers on a 1–100 square.

### Plenary   *whole class: about 10 minutes*

Say some numbers aloud, one at a time. Prompt the children to identify whether the numbers are odd or even. Give them about ten numbers orally to identify, each time asking the child who responds to say how they know and which rule was used.

Ask individual children to complete some calculations such as these on the board:

$8 + 6$    $9 + 5$    $23 + 21$    $42 + 14$    $17 + 3$    $18 + 12$

Each time, ask the child to say whether the numbers to be added together are odd or even and whether the answer is odd or even.

Ask the children if they notice anything about the answers to the calculations on the board. If no one is able to generalize, then try some more similar calculations until the children realize that they are all even numbers.
*Can anyone explain why the sum of 2 even numbers is always even and the sum of 2 odd numbers is always even?*

Demonstrate this with interlocking cubes and explain that the rule can help them to check whether calculations are correct.

### Further activities

- Ask the children:
  *Are we an odd class or an even class?*
  Investigate interesting numerical data which can be classified as odd or even, for example, the number of children in the class, house numbers, ages in months, heights in centimetres, numbers of children in the family and birthday months.

- Develop this activity by putting the information onto a simple computer database, before sorting and interpreting the data.

## Odd and even numbers

Write the missing numbers in these sequences.
Are the sequences odd or even?

odd or even?

| 14 | 16 | 18 |  |  |  |  |  |  |
|----|----|----|--|--|--|--|--|--|

|  |  | 31 | 33 |  | 37 |  |  |  |
|--|--|----|----|--|----|--|--|--|

| 60 |  |  | 54 | 52 |  |  |  |  |
|----|--|--|----|----|--|--|--|--|

|  |  |  | 57 | 59 |  | 63 |  |  |
|--|--|--|----|----|--|----|--|--|

Sort the numbers 1 to 30 on this Venn diagram.

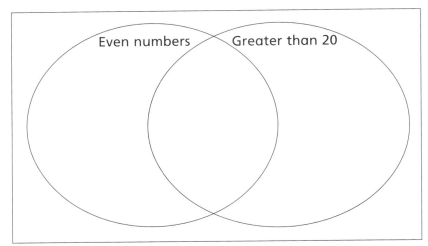

Now answer these and link them with a line to say if they are odd or even.

6 + 9 = [ 15 ]

4 + 8 = [    ]

7 + 7 = [    ]

4 + 9 = [    ]

5 + 7 = [    ]

Odd

Even

8 + 8 = [    ]

6 + 4 = [    ]

3 + 9 = [    ]

5 + 6 = [    ]

4 + 7 = [    ]

Name: ...................................................................................................................

**3b**

## Odd and even numbers

Complete this addition square.

Look for any patterns you can see.

Use the square to help you to complete these:

even or odd?

even + even = [ ]

even + odd = [ ]

odd + odd = [ ]

odd + even = [ ]

| +  | 1 | 2 | 3 | 4 | 5 | 6 | 7 | 8 | 9 | 10 |
|----|---|---|---|---|---|---|---|---|---|----|
| 1  |   |   |   |   |   |   | 8 |   |   |    |
| 2  |   |   | 5 |   |   |   |   |   |   |    |
| 3  |   |   |   |   |   |   |   |   |   |    |
| 4  |   |   |   |   |   |   |   |   |   |    |
| 5  |   |   |   |   |   | 11 |  |   |   |    |
| 6  |   |   |   |   |   |   |   |   |   |    |
| 7  |   |   |   |   |   |   |   | 15 |  |    |
| 8  |   |   |   |   |   |   |   |   |   |    |
| 9  |   |   |   | 13 |  |   |   |   |   |    |
| 10 |   |   |   |   |   |   |   | 18 |  |    |

✂ - - - - - - - - - - - - - - - - - - - - - - - - - - - - - - - - - - - - - - - - - -

Name: ...................................................................................................................

**3c**

## Odd and even numbers

You need: a yellow pencil

Write the missing numbers on this 1–100 square.

Colour all the even numbers yellow.

Write about any pattern you can see.

[ ]

| 1  | 2  | 3  | 4  |    |    | 7  |    |    | 10  |
|----|----|----|----|----|----|----|----|----|-----|
| 11 |    |    | 15 |    |    |    |    | 19 |     |
|    | 22 |    | 24 | 25 | 26 |    |    |    | 30  |
|    | 33 |    |    |    | 37 |    | 39 |    |     |
| 41 |    | 44 |    |    | 47 | 48 |    |    |     |
|    | 52 | 53 |    | 55 |    |    |    | 59 | 60  |
|    | 62 | 63 |    |    | 66 | 67 |    |    | 70  |
|    |    | 75 |    |    |    |    |    |    |     |
| 81 |    | 85 |    | 87 |    |    |    |    |     |
|    | 92 | 93 |    | 96 |    |    |    |    | 100 |

Key Lessons in Numeracy:
Numbers and the Number System Year 3

**Counting patterns**

**Lesson objective**

- to count on in steps of 3, 4 or 5 from any small number to at least 50, and then back again

**Language**

- sequence, pattern, predict, count on, count back

**Resources**

- class number line (Resource sheet 6), class 1–100 square (Resource sheet 3), **PCM4a, 4b, 4c**

**Prior learning**

- counting in ones, tens and hundreds
- counting on and back in twos, threes, fours and fives to 30

**Teaching**    *whole class: about 15 minutes*

- Explain to the children that this lesson is about counting forwards (counting on) and backwards (counting back) in steps of different sizes.

- With reference to the number line or 1–100 square, if necessary, ask the class to:

  *Start at 0 and count on in twos to 50 and back.*

  *Start at 0 and count on in fives to 50 and back.*

- *Start at 4 and count on in fives to 49 and back.*

  Write the last sequence out on the board. Explain that it is a sequence of numbers and that in this sequence each number is 5 more than the previous number. Point out that the numbers in the sequence increase by 5 each time.

  *Can you see a pattern in the numbers?*

  *Start at 3 and count on in fives to 53 and back.*

  *What do you notice about this sequence? What would the pattern be if we started at 5? What if we started at 2? Can anyone explain the pattern?*

- Explain to the children that they are now going to count on in steps of 3. Demonstrate how to use the number line to help with this, then ask the children to:

  *Start at 1 and count on in threes to 40 and back.*

  *Start at 2 and count on in threes to 47 and back.*

  *Can you see a pattern with this number sequence?*

- Show the class how to use the number line to help them to count on in fours, then ask them to:

  *Start at 0 and count on in fours to 52 and back to 0.*

  *Start at 3 and count on in fours to 51 and back to 3.*

  *Can you see a pattern with this sequence?*

- Now explain that the activities they will be doing involve counting in steps of different sizes and that you will be asking them to talk about any patterns they notice at the end of the lesson.

**Activities**    *about 15 minutes*

**Core** (for whole class or average attainers)

Give out **PCM4a** and tell the children that they are going to practise continuing number sequences in threes, fours and fives. Remind then to look for patterns in the numbers as they proceed.

Key Lessons in Numeracy: Numbers and the Number System Year 3

## Extension (for extension lesson or higher attainers)

Provide copies of **PCM4b** and tell the children they will be completing counting sequences and explaining how the sequences work, before making up their own sequences counting in threes, fours and fives.

## Support (for reinforcement lesson or lower attainers)

Give the children **PCM4c**. Complete a few oral counts in fives and threes similar to those at the beginning of the lesson and using the 1–100 square. Then explain that they are going to practise counting in fives and threes from both given numbers and numbers of their own choosing, recording their results on the **PCM**. Remind them to try to look for any patterns and be ready to talk about them at the end of the lesson. Tell them they can work either in pairs or individually on the task.

**Plenary**        *whole class: about 10 minutes*

Ask the children who used **PCM4a** or **PCM4c** to talk about the patterns they noticed in their work. Ask them to predict the next few numbers in each sequence. Explain that noticing patterns in number sequences can help to predict how the sequence will continue.

## Further activities

● Play 'Guess the rule', a game for the whole class or small groups. Each child makes up and records a sequence of six numbers (it cannot be a random selection of numbers) but does not allow anyone else to see it. The players then take turns to enter any two numbers from their own sequence on a row of six boxes which the other players can see. The rest of the group takes turns to suggest other numbers that are in the sequence. If a suggestion is correct, it is written in the appropriate place but if not, it is written in a drawing of a dustbin. The aim is to discover the rule of the sequence before five numbers appear in the dustbin.

Name: ..............................................................................................

4a

## Counting patterns

Continue these number sequences.

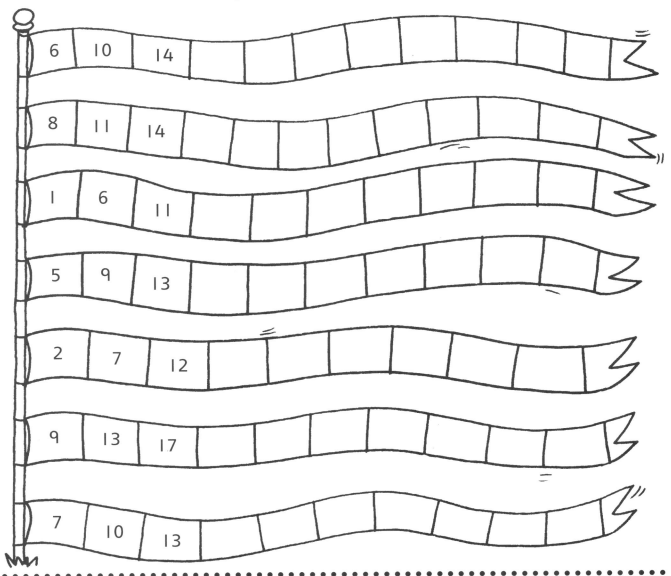

6 10 14

8 11 14

1 6 11

5 9 13

2 7 12

9 13 17

7 10 13

Now make up your own sequences in the same way.

**Key Lessons in Numeracy:**
Numbers and the Number System Year 3

Name: ...........................................................................................................

## Counting patterns

Copy and complete these number sequences.
Write a sentence with each one to explain how you worked it out.

1 | | | 18 | 23 | | 33 | | | |  _____

2 | | | 15 | 19 | | | 31 | | |  _____

3 | | | | 17 | | | 26 | 29 | |  _____

4 | | | 36 | | 26 | 21 | | | |  _____

5 | | | | 38 | 34 | | | 22 | |  _____

Now make up five more sequences of your own using different steps.

- - - - - - - - - - - - - - - - - - - - - - - - - - - - - - - - - - - - - - - - - - - ✂

Name: ...........................................................................................................

## Counting patterns

Complete these number sequences by counting on in fives.

| 3 | | | | | | | | | |
| 6 | | | | | | | | | |

Choose a number and count on in fives. ▶

| | | | | | | | | | |

Complete these number sequences by counting on in threes.

| 8 | | | | | | | | | |
| 10 | | | | | | | | | |

Choose a number and count on in threes. ▶

| | | | | | | | | | |

**Key Lessons in Numeracy:**
Numbers and the Number System Year 3

### Lesson objective

- to recognize 2-digit multiples of 2, 5 and 10

### Language

- multiple, in common, rule, divisible

### Resources

- class 1–100 square (Resource sheet 3), individual fan numbers or digit cards (Resource sheets 1 and 2), large blank Venn diagram drawn on the board, **PCM5a, 5b, 5c**

### Prior learning

- recognizing multiples of 5 and 10
- using a Venn diagram for two criteria

**Teaching**        *whole class: about 20 minutes*

- Explain to the children that this lesson is about recognizing multiples of particular numbers.

- Begin by finding out if the children know what 'multiple' means and establish clearly that a multiple of a number is exactly divisible by that number.

- Ask the children to say aloud all the multiples of 10 to 100. Point to the numbers on the 1–100 square as they do so.
  *What do all the multiples of 10 have in common?*

- Ask the children to say all the multiples of 5 to 100. Point to the numbers on the 1–100 square as they do so.
  *What do multiples of 5 end with?* (5 or 10)

- Ask them to say all the multiples of 2 to 50. Point to the numbers on the 1–100 square as they do so.
  *What do multiples of 2 end with?* (0, 2, 4, 6 or 8 – an even number)

- Now write the following statements on the board and ask individual children to complete them:

  Multiples of 10 end with __.

  Multiples of 5 end with __ or __.

  Multiples of 2 end with __ __ __ __ or __.

  Ask the children to identify which numbers the following are multiples of, by holding up the appropriate fan numbers or digit cards (for example, 5 is a multiple of 50).

  80    42    75    60    58    30    55    10    and so on.

  Ask individuals to explain how they know. Discuss the fact that multiples of 10 are also multiples of 2 and 5.

- Reveal the Venn diagram on the board and remind the children how it works.

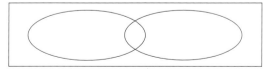

  The left-hand circle is for the set of numbers which are multiples of 2, the right-hand circle for multiples of 5, and the intersection for multiples of both 2 and 5. The surrounding rectangle is for numbers which are not multiples of either 2 or 5.

  Say aloud some numbers and ask the children where they should be placed. Ask individuals to write a further six or seven numbers on the diagram.

**Core** (for whole class or average attainers)

Hand out **PCM5a**. Explain to the children that they will be recording numbers on Venn diagrams, like the one on the board. When they have completed the Venn diagrams, ask the following questions for each one:

*What do you notice about the numbers in the intersection?*

*What are they all multiples of?*

**Extension** (for extension lesson or higher attainers)

Give the children **PCM5b**. Tell them that they will be recording numbers on a Venn diagram using three criteria. Establish that they understand the activity before they begin. Return to the group when they have completed the activity to discuss the diagrams. Ask them to explain why the multiples of 10 are all in the intersection.

**Support** (for reinforcement lesson or lower attainers)

Hand out **PCM5c**. Describe to the children that they are going to count on in twos from 2 and colour these multiples on the 1–100 square. They should circle all the multiples of 5, and put a cross on the multiples of 10. Stay with the group for a few minutes to make sure the children understand that they are looking for the pattern of the multiples.

**Plenary**    *whole class: about 5 minutes*

Write these numbers on the board:

35    50    65    25    30    95    75

*What do these numbers have in common?*

Make sure that the response includes the word *multiple*. Ask one child to write 'multiples of 5' next to or below the numbers on the board.

*How do you know they are multiples of 5? What is the rule for recognizing multiples of 5?*

Repeat this activity for multiples of 2 and 10.

Remind the class that they understand the word *multiple* and that they should use it in the future whenever it is appropriate.

## Further activities

- Investigate the sums of consecutive numbers. Provide sets of three consecutive numbers and ask the children to add them together. For example:
  *6 + 7 + 8 = 21*
  *8 + 9 + 10 = 27*
  *3 + 4 + 5 = 12*

*Do you notice a pattern?*
Record the information on the board to show the results clearly.

- Repeat the activity using sets of five consecutive numbers.

Name: .........................................................................................

5a

## Recognizing 2-digit multiples

Write these sets of numbers in each Venn diagram.

30    42    45
19    80    5    26
57    55    70
90    98    15
6    45

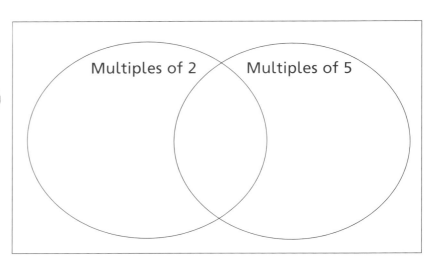

Multiples of 2    Multiples of 5

50    38    40
25    32    19    35
88    75    80
85    27    21
90    5

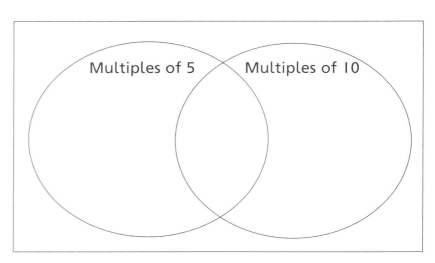

Multiples of 5    Multiples of 10

30    85    38
60    70    20    46
81    35    92
63    80    40
50    74

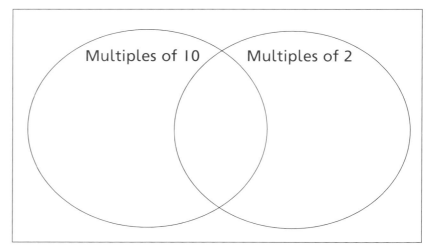

Multiples of 10    Multiples of 2

**Key Lessons in Numeracy:**
Numbers and the Number System Year 3

## Recognizing 2-digit multiples

Write the numbers 1 to 100 in this Venn diagram.

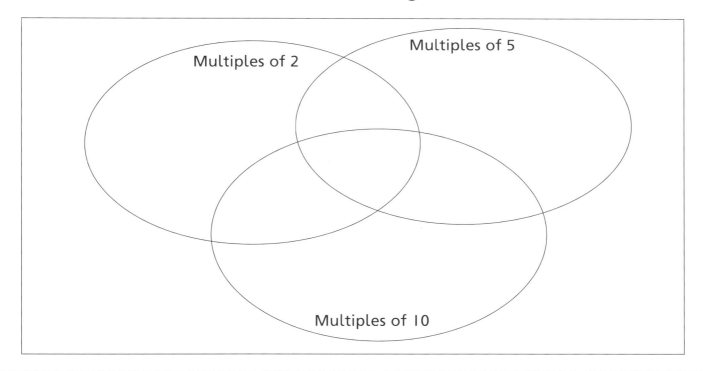

- - - - - - - - - - - - - - - - - - - - - - - - - - - - - - - - - - - - - - - - - - - - - - - ✂

## Recognizing 2-digit multiples

| You need: a yellow pencil |
|---|

Colour in the multiples of 2 in yellow.

Circle the multiples of 5.

Put a cross on the multiples of 10.

What do you notice?

| 1 | 2 | 3 | 4 | 5 | 6 | 7 | 8 | 9 | 10 |
|---|---|---|---|---|---|---|---|---|---|
| 11 | 12 | 13 | 14 | 15 | 16 | 17 | 18 | 19 | 20 |
| 21 | 22 | 23 | 24 | 25 | 26 | 27 | 28 | 29 | 30 |
| 31 | 32 | 33 | 34 | 35 | 36 | 37 | 37 | 39 | 40 |
| 41 | 42 | 43 | 44 | 45 | 46 | 47 | 48 | 49 | 50 |
| 51 | 52 | 53 | 54 | 55 | 56 | 57 | 58 | 59 | 60 |
| 61 | 62 | 63 | 64 | 65 | 66 | 67 | 68 | 69 | 70 |
| 71 | 72 | 73 | 74 | 75 | 76 | 77 | 78 | 79 | 80 |
| 81 | 82 | 83 | 84 | 85 | 86 | 87 | 88 | 89 | 90 |
| 91 | 92 | 93 | 94 | 95 | 96 | 97 | 98 | 99 | 100 |

**Key Lessons in Numeracy:**
Numbers and the Number System Year 3

# Recognizing 3-digit multiples

## Lesson objective

- to recognize 3-digit multiples of 2, 5, 10, 50 and 100

## Language

- multiple, in common, rule, Carroll diagram

## Resources

- counting stick, **PCM6a, 6b, 6c**

## Prior learning

- recognizing 2-digit multiples of 2, 5 and 10
- using a Venn diagram for two criteria

---

**Teaching**　　*whole class: about 20 minutes*

- Explain to the children that this lesson is about recognizing 3-digit multiples of particular numbers.

- Ask the children what *multiple* means. If necessary, remind them that a multiple of a number is exactly divisible by that number.

  Hold up a counting stick and name one end 0, the other end 100. Ask the children to say aloud the multiples of 10 up to 100 and point to the lines on the counting stick as they do so.

  *What do all the multiples of 10 have in common?*

- Now name one end of the stick 0 and the other end 1000. Ask the children to say aloud the multiples of 100 up to 1000 as you point to each division.

  *What do all the multiples of 100 have in common?*

- Name one end of the counting stick 100 and the other end 150. Ask the children to say aloud the multiples of 5 from 100 up to 150 as you point to each division.

  *What do all the multiples of 5 end with?*

- Repeat the activity with multiples of 50, naming one end of the stick 0 and the other 500.

  Ask them the rule for any multiples of 2. If they are not sure, ask what multiples of 2 end with and make sure they realize it is 0, 2, 4, 6, or 8.

  *Is this true for any multiple of 2?*

- Now write the following statements on the board and ask individual children to complete them:

  Multiples of 10 end with __.

  Multiples of 100 end with __.

  Multiples of 5 end with __ or __.

  Multiples of 50 end with __ or __.

  Multiples of 2 end with __ __ __ __ or __.

---

**Activities**　　*about 15 minutes*

**Core** (for whole class or average attainers)

Explain to the children that they will be recording numbers on a Carroll diagram. Give them **PCM6a**, establishing that they understand how a Carroll diagram works and how to fill one in before they begin.

**Extension** (for extension lesson or higher attainers)

Tell the children that they will be recording numbers on a Carroll diagram using three criteria. Give them **PCM5b** and explain how it works. Establish that they understand before they begin. Return to the group just before the end of the session to discuss the diagrams.

**Support** (for reinforcement lesson or lower attainers)

Explain to the children that they are going to write five multiples of 2, 5, 10, 50 and 100 on **PCM6c**. Encourage them to think of numbers greater than 100. They should then write the rule for each of the multiples. If help is needed, remind them that the rules are written on the board. Stay with the group for a few minutes to make sure the children understand the activity.

### Plenary — *whole class: about 5 minutes*

Return to the list on the board:

Multiples of 10 end with 0.

Multiples of 100 end with 00

Multiples of 5 end with 0 or 5.

Multiples of 50 end with 00 or 50.

Multiples of 2 end with 0, 2, 4, 6 or 8.

Make sure that the children understand these rules.

Discuss the fact that: multiples of 10 are also multiples of 2 and 5; multiples of 50 are also multiples of 10, 2 and 5; and that multiples of 100 are also multiples of 10, 2, 5 and 50.

### Further activities

● Provide some problem-solving situations that involve recognizing 3-digit multiples, for example:
*There are 360 bars of chocolate in a box. The shopkeeper stacks them in equal piles.*

*In how many different ways could they be stacked?*
Record the results in a chart. Then repeat the activity using other starting numbers.

# Recognizing 3-digit multiples

Write these sets of numbers in each Carroll diagram.

105   120

148   325   172

160   200   515

223   430

179   292

|  | Multiple of 2 | Not a multiple of 2 |
|---|---|---|
| Multiple of 5 |  |  |
| Not a multiple of 5 |  |  |

140   300

620   750   400

950   900   850

190   680   150

200

|  | Multiple of 100 | Not a multiple of 100 |
|---|---|---|
| Multiple of 50 |  |  |
| Not a multiple of 50 |  |  |

220   450

635   400   800

730   142   300

840   270

315   602

|  | Multiple of 10 | Not a multiple of 10 |
|---|---|---|
| Multiple of 100 |  |  |
| Not a multiple of 100 |  |  |

Name: ...................................................................................

## Recognizing 3-digit multiples

Write these numbers in this Carroll diagram.

| 178 | 290 | 400 |
| 215 | 185 | 107 |
| 192 | 450 | 630 |
| 542 | 195 | 386 |
| 405 | 700 | 291 |
| 343 | 850 | 240 |

|  | Multiple of 2 | Not a multiple of 2 |
|---|---|---|
| Multiple of 5 | Multiple of 50 | |
| Not a multiple of 5 | | |

Now design your own multiples Carroll diagram for a partner to try.

- - - - - - - - - - - - - - - - - - - - - - - - - - - - - - - - - - - - - - - - ✂

Name: ...................................................................................

## Recognizing 3-digit multiples

Write five different multiples for each of these.

Then complete the rule for each one.

Multiples of 2: _____ _____ _____ _____ _____   end in:

Multiples of 5: _____ _____ _____ _____ _____   end in:

Multiples of 10: _____ _____ _____ _____ _____   end in:

Multiples of 50: _____ _____ _____ _____ _____   end in:

Multiples of 100: _____ _____ _____ _____ _____   end in:

**Key Lessons in Numeracy:**
Numbers and the Number System Year 3

© P. Broadbent and K.Church 1999. Heinemann Educational Ltd.
For copyright restrictions, see reverse of title page.

# Place value and ordering

## LESSON 7 · Reading and writing numbers to 1000

### Lesson objective

- to read and write whole numbers to at least 1000 in figures and words

### Language

- digit, names for numbers to 1000

### Resources

- a 3-spike abacus, individual fan numbers or digit cards (Resource sheets 1 and 2), a list of 3-digit numbers written in words on the board, lists of words for numbers displayed in the room to help with spelling (for example, a list from 0 to 9, a list from 10 to 19 and a list of multiples of 10 from 20 to 90), **PCM7a, 7b, 7c**

### Prior learning

- reading and writing numbers to at least 100

---

**Teaching**    *whole class: about 15 minutes*

- Explain to the children that this lesson is about reading and writing numbers to 1000 in figures and in words.

- Write a 3-digit number on the board in words and ask one of the children to read it. Ask another child to write the number as a numeral. Demonstrate to the children how the number is shown on the abacus and remind them that the three columns represent hundreds, tens and units. The beads on the left show how many hundreds there are, the next spike shows the number of tens and the right-hand spike shows the number of ones. Relate this to the numeral on the board. (This needs to be made explicit to overcome the problem which some children have of writing a number such as 437 as 40037.)

- Write another 3-digit number on the board in words and ask one of the children to read it. Ask another child to write the number as a numeral. Repeat this activity using a few more 3-digit numbers, making sure you include some numbers with no tens or no units, or both.

- Say some 3-digit numbers aloud and ask the children to show you the number using their fan numbers or digit cards. Clarify and correct any misunderstandings as they arise.

- Reveal the list of numbers written in words on the board and ask the children to show you each number in turn using their fan numbers or digit cards.

---

**Activities**    *about 15 minutes*

**Core** (for whole class or average attainers)

Give the children **PMC7a**. Tell them to complete the cross-number, similar to a crossword, by writing the numbers given in words in the clues as numerals in the grid. Make sure the children also understand the second half of the sheet where, this time, they write the clues to given answers. Point out the word lists on display to help with any spelling difficulties up to ninety-nine.

---

**Extension** (for extension lesson or higher attainers)

Explain to the children that they will be identifying numbers by following the clues on **PCM7b**, then writing them in both numerals and in words. When this is finished, encourage them to make up some of their own clues for a partner to identify.

**Support** (for reinforcement lesson or lower attainers)

Begin by drawing attention to the word lists on display round the class to help with spelling and asking individual children to point to particular words as you say them.

Give the children **PCM7c** and explain that they have four things to do for each number written in words on the sheet.

1. They should read the number.

2. They then copy the writing.

3. They write the number as a numeral in the box.

4. Finally, they represent the number by drawing beads on each spike of the abacus. Stay with the group a few minutes to make sure the children are comfortable with the activity.

**Plenary**　　*whole class: about 10 minutes*

Ask the children to talk about any difficulties they had with their work and clarify and correct any misunderstandings.

Say some numbers aloud and ask the children to use their fan numbers or digit cards to show you numbers. Include 1-, 2- and 3-digit numbers and make sure that many of the numbers contain 0 in different places.

**Further activities**

● Ask the children to make up their own cross-numbers, and to write the clues.

● Make a display of 3-digit numbers in context, cut out from newspapers and magazines. The children then work in pairs or groups to write the number in words beside each example.

Name: .................................................................................................

**7a**

# Reading and writing numbers to 1000

Write the answers to this cross-number.

*Across*

1 seven hundred and twenty-five
3 two hundred and ninety-four
5 one hundred and sixty-seven
6 one hundred and twenty-four
8 one hundred and twenty-six
10 two hundred and ninety-three
12 seven hundred and eight
14 three hundred and forty
15 five hundred and three
16 two hundred and ninety

*Down*

1 seven hundred and forty-one
2 five hundred and fourteen
3 two hundred and seventy-one
4 four hundred and six
7 two hundred and nineteen
9 two hundred and ninety
10 two hundred and five
11 three hundred and thirty-three
12 seven hundred and two
13 eight hundred and twenty

Now write the clues for this cross-number.

*Across*

1 _____

3 _____

*Down*

1 _____

2 _____

**Key Lessons in Numeracy:**
Numbers and the Number System Year 3

Name: ....................................................................................................... **7b**

## Reading and writing numbers to 1000

Read the clues below and write the numbers as numerals and as words.

I have 6 hundreds, 8 tens and a single unit. What number am I?

I have no units, 5 tens and 2 hundreds. What number am I?

My hundreds and tens digits are the same and total 10. My units digit is the next even digit after 6. What number am I?

I have no tens digit and the other two digits total 9. I am a number between 100 and 120. What number am I?

Now make up your own clues for numbers.

- - - - - - - - - - - - - - - - - - - - - - - - - - - - - - - - - - - - - - - - - - - - - - - - - - - - - - - - - - - - - - ✂

Name: ....................................................................................................... **7c**

## Reading and writing numbers to 1000

Complete these, following your teacher's instructions.

three hundred and forty-seven

H   T   U

two hundred and thirty

H   T   U

eight hundred and sixty-one
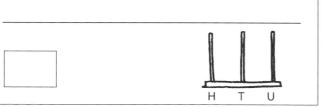
H   T   U

five hundred and nine

H   T   U

**Key Lessons in Numeracy:**
Numbers and the Number System Year 3

**Recognizing hundreds, tens and units**

### Lesson objective

- to know what each digit in a 3-digit number represents (HTU)

### Language

- digit, 1-digit number, 2-digit number, 3-digit number, names for numbers to 1000

### Resources

- 3-spike abacus, counters, decahedral dice (numbered from 0 to 9), individual fan numbers or digit cards (Resource sheets 1 and 2), **PCM8a, 8b, 8c**

### Prior learning

- knowing what each digit in a 2-digit number represents

---

### Teaching — *whole class: about 15 minutes*

- Explain to the children that this lesson is about knowing what the individual digits in numbers mean.

- Write a set of five 2-digit numbers on the board and ask the children to order them from the smallest to the greatest.

  *Which digit do we look at first when we put numbers in order of size? What does the left-hand digit in each number mean?*

  It is most important for their understanding that children recognize that in a number such as 53, the 5 means 'fifty'. The 5 is in the tens place and, as such, represents 5 tens, but its value is that of the number which we call 'fifty'.

  Repeat the activity for a set of 3-digit numbers and ask similar questions.

- Show the children 132 represented on the abacus.

  *What is this number? If I move one of the unit beads and put it on the hundred spike, will the new number be bigger or smaller than 132? What if I put the hundred bead on the unit spike? What will the new number be? Is that bigger or smaller than 132? What if I move one of the tens beads?*

- Ask three children each to give you a single digit and write them on the board. (Keep a space between each number so that they do not appear as a 3-digit number.)

  *Which numbers can we make with all three digits? What is the largest number we can make? What is the smallest number?*

  Repeat the activity using different sets of three digits.

---

### Activities — *about 15 minutes*

**Core** (for whole class or average attainers)

Give the children **PCM8a**. Tell the children that they will be making different numbers by placing a given number of counters on a picture of a spike abacus, then recording them as numerals in order of increasing size. Explain that they should make as many different numbers as they can for each given number of counters, then write the numbers in order of size before going on to the next one. For example, 2 counters can make 2, 11 and 20. Make sure they are clear that they do not draw on the abacus, but just rest their counters on the picture.

**Extension** (for extension lesson or higher attainers)

Tell the children that they will be playing games in pairs using the decahedral dice. Give them **PCM8b** to record their scores. Explain that in the first game, the players take turns to roll the dice and record the number as one digit of a 3-digit number in one of the boxes. Each player has three turns, and the player with the highest 3-digit number wins. They have four attempts at this game. In the second game, they have to throw the dice in turn nine times to make three 3-digit numbers, then add the numbers together. The player with the highest total wins the game. The third game is similar to the first game, but the aim is to get the lowest number. Remind them to consider the strategy of where to place the number each time. As a development, the players can choose whether to keep the digit they roll or give it to their opponent, continuing to throw the dice alternately.

**Support** (for reinforcement lesson or lower attainers)

Tell the children that they will be writing sets of numbers in order of size, starting with the smallest. Remind them that the 100 digit is the most important one when thinking about the size of a number, and that if two numbers have the same hundreds digit, the tens digit is the next most important, and so on. Show the children two different 3-digit numbers and ask:

*Which is the larger? How do you know?*

Repeat the activity for another pair of 3-digit numbers, then for a set of three 3-digit numbers, then four 3-digit numbers, ordering the numbers when there are more than two. When you are satisfied that the children understand, give them **PCM9c**, explaining that they have to look at the first set of numbers then write the numbers down in order of size before going on to the second set.

**Plenary**     *whole class: about 10 minutes*

Say a variety of 3-digit numbers and ask the children to show you the number of hundreds, the number of tens and the number of units using fan numbers or digit cards.

Ask the children to show you numbers from general instructions such as:

*This number has more hundreds than tens, and more tens than units.*

Do this for different numbers and ask the children to show you the number they have made. Discuss the different numbers being shown and ask the children whether they fulfil the criteria you gave.

Explain that understanding the value of individual digits in numbers is called *place value* and that it is a very important part of their learning about number. They need to use place value when they do mental calculations, for example, when adding 341 and 225 together, there are 5 hundreds, 6 tens and 6 units making a total of 566. Point out that knowledge of place value enables sums like these to be done mentally.

**Further activities**

- Investigate all the numbers that can be made from any three different digits. Record them in order of increasing size. *How many 3-digit numbers can be made?*

*How many 1- and 2-digit numbers? How many altogether? What if two of the digits are the same? What if one of the digits is 0?*

Name: ...................................................................................

## Recognizing hundreds, tens and units

You need: some counters

Place the counters on this abacus to show the different numbers.

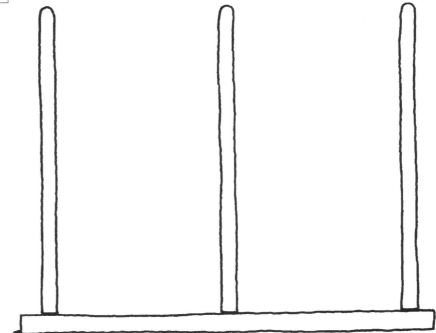

Write all the numbers in order of increasing size that can be made from:

2 counters

3 counters

4 counters

5 counters

## Recognizing hundreds, tens and units

You will need: decahedral dice

**Game 1**
Highest number

Throw the dice
three times.

a ☐☐☐   b ☐☐☐   c ☐☐☐   d ☐☐☐

**Game 2**
Highest total

Throw the dice
nine times.

☐☐☐ + ☐☐☐ + ☐☐☐ = ☐☐☐

**Game 3**
Lowest number

Throw the dice
three times.

a ☐☐☐   b ☐☐☐   c ☐☐☐   d ☐☐☐

---

Name: .............................................................................

8c

## Recognizing hundreds, tens and units

Write these sets of numbers in order of size, starting with the smallest.

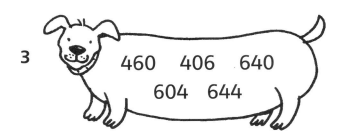

1   384   296   348
    308   280

2   298   480   350
    341   209

\_\_\_\_   \_\_\_\_   \_\_\_\_

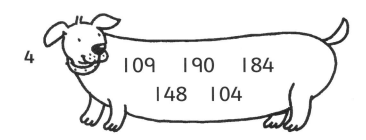

3   460   406   640
    604   644

4   109   190   184
    148   104

\_\_\_\_   \_\_\_\_   \_\_\_\_

**Key Lessons in Numeracy:**
Numbers and the Number System Year 3

### Lesson objective

- to partition 3-digit numbers into a multiple of 100, a multiple of 10 and units (HTU)

### Language

- place value, digit, names for numbers to 1000

### Resources

- a larger set of arrow cards for the teacher to use for demonstration, individual sets of arrow cards (Resource sheet 4), a list on the board of about six numbers with partitioned equivalents such as:

  $274 = \_\_ + 70 + 4$;  $359 = 300 + \_\_ + 9$;
  $863 = 800 + 60 + \_\_$

  lists of words for numbers to help with spelling displayed in the room (see Lesson 7, Reading and writing numbers to 1000), **PCM9a, 9b, 9c**

### Prior learning

- partitioning 2-digit numbers

### Teaching — *whole class: about 10 minutes*

- Explain to the children that this lesson is about knowing more about place value.

- Show the children a 3-digit number using the large set of arrow cards. Ask them what each digit represents, and then take out the appropriate card to reveal the value of the digit. Repeat for other 3-digit numbers. Explain how the arrow cards work.

  Give out the individual sets of arrow cards and ask the children to show you a variety of numbers which you say. For example:

  *Show me 279. How many hundreds are there? What is the value of the 7?*

  Ask about the value of individual digits in the numbers and ask the children to check each answer by removing the appropriate card.

- Reveal the list of equations on the board and ask the children to show you the missing numbers by using their arrow cards.

### Activities — *about 20 minutes*

**Core** (for whole class or average attainers)

Explain to the children that they will be identifying numbers from pictures of separate arrow cards, and then showing how numbers can be split up to give the value of their digits. Give them **PCM9a** and make sure they understand both sections before they begin.

**Extension** (for extension lesson or higher attainers)

Explain that for any three digits, different numbers can be made depending on the position of each digit. Hand out **PCM9b** and ask them to try to find six different numbers for each set of digits. They can then explore numbers with two digits the same.

**Support** (for reinforcement lesson or lower attainers)

Give the children **PCM9c**. Tell the children that they will be making up given 3-digit numbers with their arrow cards and recording them on the **PCM**. They then write the numbers in words. Before they begin, demonstrate how to record a number on the sheet and remind them that there are lists of words in the classroom to help with spelling.

**Plenary**     *whole class: about 10 minutes*

Say some numbers aloud and ask the children to use their arrow cards to show you the number. Explain that they have learned more about place value today to help them when they calculate.

**Further activities**

● Play 'Arrow card bingo'. Each player makes a 3-digit number with their arrow cards. The teacher places a full set of arrow cards (HTU) in a bag and takes one card out at random. This is shown to the class and the number called out, for example: *Thirty.*

The children whose 3-digit number includes 30 remove the 30 card and place it in front of them. This is repeated and continued until a player has had all three arrow cards called out. This player shouts **Bingo!** and is the winner.

# Partitioning 3-digit numbers

Write what number each set of three arrows shows.

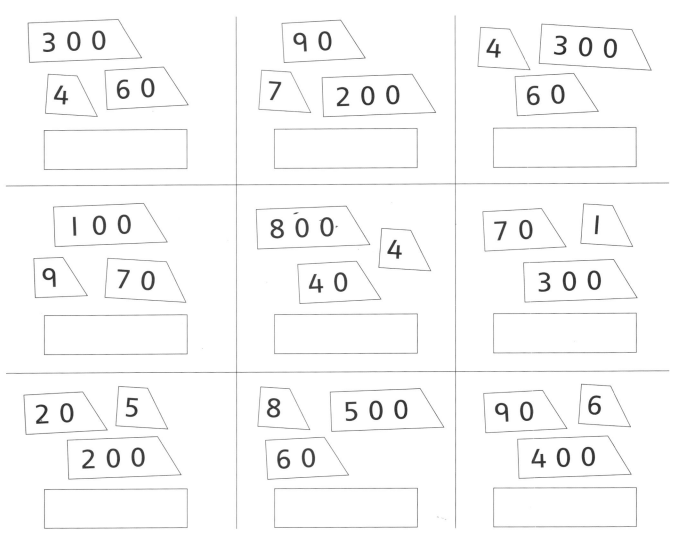

· · · · · · · · · · · · · · · · · · · · · · · · · · · · · · · · · · · · · · · · · · · · · · · · · · ·

Now show these numbers on the arrow cards.

274 = ☐ + ☐ + ☐          697 = ☐ + ☐ + ☐

851 = ☐ + ☐ + ☐          452 = ☐ + ☐ + ☐

723 = ☐ + ☐ + ☐          395 = ☐ + ☐ + ☐

947 = ☐ + ☐ + ☐          681 = ☐ + ☐ + ☐

211 = ☐ + ☐ + ☐          957 = ☐ + ☐ + ☐

**Key Lessons in Numeracy:**
Numbers and the Number System Year 3

Name: .................................................................................................

## Partitioning 3-digit numbers

Write the numbers you can make from these sets of 3 digits.

| 3 | 4 | 5 |

| 2 | 9 | 6 |

☐ + ☐ + ☐ = _____     ☐ + ☐ + ☐ = _____

☐ + ☐ + ☐ = _____     ☐ + ☐ + ☐ = _____

☐ + ☐ + ☐ = _____     ☐ + ☐ + ☐ = _____

☐ + ☐ + ☐ = _____     ☐ + ☐ + ☐ = _____

☐ + ☐ + ☐ = _____     ☐ + ☐ + ☐ = _____

☐ + ☐ + ☐ = _____     ☐ + ☐ + ☐ = _____

Now use three of your own digits. What if two of the digits are the same?

---

Name: .................................................................................................

## Partitioning 3-digit numbers

Make these numbers on the arrow cards. Then write the numbers as words.

251 = ☐ + ☐ + ☐     <u>two hundred and</u>
_____

729 = ☐ + ☐ + ☐     _____
_____

468 = ☐ + ☐ + ☐     _____
_____

887 = ☐ + ☐ + ☐     _____
_____

## Lesson objective

- to compare any two 3-digit numbers, say which is more or less, and give a number which lies between them

## Language

- more than, less than, greater than, fewer than, between, smaller, largest

## Resources

- large counting stick for the teacher to use (for example, a blank metre stick marked in 10 equal sections), individual counting strips for the children to use (a strip of card about ruler size, marked in 10 equal sections, with a rubber band to use as a slide indicator), individual fan numbers or digit cards (Resource sheets 1 and 2), **PCM10a, 10b, 10c**

## Prior learning

- understanding place value in 3-digit numbers

### Teaching *whole class: about 10 minutes*

- Explain to the children that this lesson is about ordering and comparing the size of different numbers.

- Hold up the counting stick and explain that one end of the stick is 0, the other end is 10. Point to the middle and ask the children to name the number.

  Now tell the children that the values on the stick are changing – one end is 20 and the other end is 40.

  *What is the middle number now?*

  Repeat the activity for different ranges of numbers, for example, half-way between: 100 and 200; 85 and 95; 3 and 4; 450 and 550.

- Ask the children to indicate the following numbers on their counting strips as follows:

  *The left-hand side is 0 and the right-hand side is 10. Show me where 5 is. Show me where 4 is. Show me where 8 is.*

- *The left-hand side is 0 and the right-hand side is 100. Show me where 50 is. Show me where 70 is, and where 75 is. Show me a number which is greater than 80. Show me a number which is fewer than 20. Show me a number between 50 and 60.*

- *The left-hand side is 0 and the right-hand side is 1000. Show me where 500 lies. Show me where to find 200. Show me where 800 is. Show me a number which is larger than 800. Show me a number smaller than 400. Show me a number between 600 and 700.*

- Write 246 and 624 on the board. Ask:

  *Which is the larger number?*

  Repeat this for other pairs of 3-digit numbers, asking:

  *How do you know?*

### Activities *about 20 minutes*

**Core** (for whole class or average attainers)

Explain to the children that they will be finding middle numbers on number lines, and ordering groups of numbers. Give them **PCM10a** to complete.

**Extension** (for extension lesson or higher attainers)

Hand out **PCM10b**. Tell the children that they will be using clues to find particular numbers on number lines, before making up some similar puzzles for a partner to solve.

**Support** (for reinforcement lesson or lower attainers)

Explain to the children that they will be finding all the whole numbers which come between two given numbers. Give them **PCM10c**, and explain the first example. Stay with the children as they begin the activity to make sure they understand that they need to find all the numbers. When they have finished the examples on the **PCM**, they can make up some similar puzzles for a partner to solve.

### Plenary — *whole class: about 10 minutes*

Using their fan numbers or digit cards, ask the children to show you a number which is:

– *greater than 457*

– *less than 100*

– *between 560 and 570*

– *bigger than 3*

– *smaller than 200*

– *between 395 and 402*

– *halfway between 95 and 105*

– *halfway between 800 and 850*

and so on.

Explain to the children that they should now be able to use all the numbers to 1000.

### Further activities

- Show the children a road map which gives distances between towns and cities. Compare distances asking questions using appropriate language, such as:
  *Which cities are more than 500 kilometres from each other?*
  *Which cities are less than 200 kilometres from each other?*
  *Which cities are between 300 kilometres and 500 kilometres from each other?*

- Play 'What's my number?' Give each child a set of fan numbers and ask them to make any 3-digit number. The teacher then makes a number, hiding it from the class, and gives clues, such as:
  *My number is greater than 500.*
  The children check their number and change it, if necessary, in an attempt to match the teacher's number. Further clues are given until all the children have matched the teacher's number.

## Comparing and ordering numbers

Write the middle numbers on these number lines.

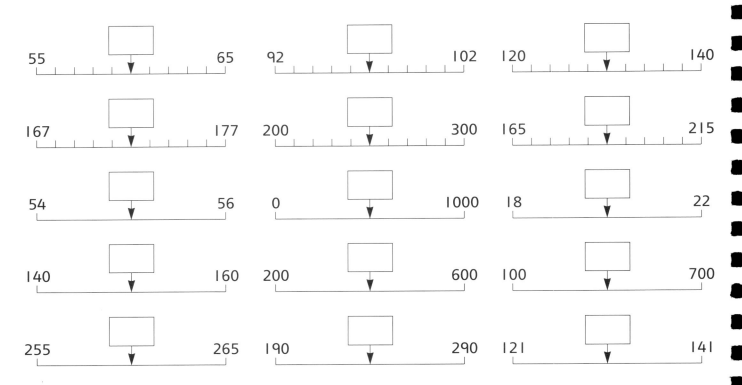

55 [ ] 65    92 [ ] 102    120 [ ] 140

167 [ ] 177    200 [ ] 300    165 [ ] 215

54 [ ] 56    0 [ ] 1000    18 [ ] 22

140 [ ] 160    200 [ ] 600    100 [ ] 700

255 [ ] 265    190 [ ] 290    121 [ ] 141

• • • • • • • • • • • • • • • • • • • • • • • • • • • • • • • • • • • • • •

Write these sets of numbers in order of size. Start with the smallest.

284    185
180    87    204
871

741    471
411    477    417
714

_____    _____

815    518
857    758    157
185

384    483
680    608    806
348

_____    _____

**Key Lessons in Numeracy:**
Numbers and the Number System Year 3

## Comparing and ordering numbers

Read the clues to find the number. Write the number in the box.

Then draw a line from the number in the box to the correct place on the number line.

754 [    ] 764

- greater than 760
- digits total 15

186 [    ] 196

- half-way between 186 and 196

200 [    ] 700

- smaller than 500
- digits total 8

130 [    ] 150

- greater than 140
- digits total 9

Now make some of your own number clues for a partner, like these.

- - - - - - - - - - - - - - - - - - - - - - - - - - - - - - - - - - - - - - - - - - - - - - - - ✂

## Comparing and ordering numbers

Write all the numbers which fit each clue.

Which numbers are bigger than 4 and smaller than 8?

[                                        ]

Which numbers are greater than 25 but less than 35?

[                                        ]

Which numbers come between 98 and 106?

[                                        ]

Which numbers are smaller than 275 but greater than 264?

[                                        ]

Now make up some clues for a partner to solve.

**Key Lessons in Numeracy:**
Numbers and the Number System Year 3

**Changing numbers by 1, 10 and 100**

## Lesson objective

- to say the number that is 1, 10 or 100 more or less than any given 2- or 3-digit number

## Language

- digit, more, less, increase, decrease

## Resources

- class 1–100 square (Resource sheet 3), a large set of arrow cards for the teacher to use for demonstration, individual sets of arrow cards (Resource sheet 4), two dice (one marked 'more' on three faces and 'less' on the other three; the other marked '1' on two faces, '10' on two faces and '100' on the remaining two faces), **PCM11a, 11b, 11c**

## Prior learning

- partitioning 3-digit numbers

**Teaching**    *whole class: about 15 minutes*

- Explain to the children that this lesson is about using what they already know about place value to make numbers bigger and smaller, that is, to increase and decrease them.

- Ask the children to start at 245 and count aloud in ones to 260. Then ask them to start at 683 and count back in ones to 665.

  *What is 1 more than 251? 246? 260? 128?*

  *What is 1 less than 672? 681? 352? 139?*

  *What do you do when you increase a number by 1? Decrease by 1?*

- With reference to the 1–100 square, ask the children to:

  *Count on in tens from 0 to 100 and back to 0.*

  *Count on in tens from 4 to 94 and back to 4.*

  *Count on in tens from 27 to 97 and back to 27.*

  *What do you notice about the position of the numbers on the square when you count in tens?*

  *What is 10 more than 15? 76? 40? 29? What is 10 less than 62? 81? 50? 13?*

  *What is 1 more than 15? 76? 40? 29? What is 1 less than 62? 81? 50? 13?*

- Ask them to count on in steps of 100 from 0 to 1000 and back to 0. Then ask them to count on in steps of 100 from 28 to 928 and back to 28, then from 143 to 943 and back to 143.

  *Which digit is changed when we make a number 100 more or less?*

- Show the children a 3-digit number, for example 436, using the large set of arrow cards.

  *What is the value of the digits 4, 3 and 6? What number is 10 more than 436? Which digit do I need to change? What should I change it to? What number is 1 more than 446? Which digit do I need to change? What should I change it to? What number is 100 less than 447? Which digit do I need to change? What should I change it to?*

- Ask the children to show you a 3-digit number using their individual sets of arrow cards. Then ask them to increase or decrease the number by 1, 10 or 100. Repeat the activity so that all six options are covered.

### Core (for whole class or average attainers)

Give the children **PCM11a**. Explain that the first activity involves making numbers bigger and smaller by adding or subtracting 1, 10 or 100. The second is the completion of number sequences and the third is completion of missing numbers in grids from a 1–100 square.

### Extension (for extension lesson or higher attainers)

Explain to the children that they will be using their arrow cards to play a game. The game is played in pairs, each player making a 3-digit number with arrow cards but not allowing their opponent to see their number. Each player takes turns to ask for single digits. For example, Player A might say, 'Give me your eights' to Player B who has chosen the number 582. Player B removes the 80 card from their number and puts it with their spare arrow cards, leaving the number 502. Player A makes a new number by adding 80 using his or her arrow cards. If Player B has no 8 cards, Player A misses that go. The first player to exceed 1000, or leave the opponent with 0, wins the game. The players use **PCM11b** to record the progress of each game, and can play as many games as they have time for.

### Support (for reinforcement lesson or lower attainers)

Tell the children that they will be playing a game as a group using the two special dice (see 'Resources'). Give the children **PCM11c** explaining that each player begins with the number 456, as shown. They take turns to roll the two dice, making the number 1, 10 or 100, 'more' or 'less' according faces of the dice. A running score should be kept by each player on their **PCM**. The + and – signs can be shaded out to show if the number needs to be increased or decreased. If a player goes below 0, they are out. The first player to exceed 900 wins the game.

Ask the children to show you a number, such as 231, using their arrow cards. Encourage them to make the number bigger by 200 (by replacing the relevant arrow card) and show you the new number. Then make the number bigger by 20, making sure the children show you the new number, and then by 2.

Repeat the activity for other 3-digit numbers with low digits.

Explain that they have learned more about place value today to help them when they calculate.

### Further activities

- Each child sets up a constant on a calculator for adding or subtracting 1, 10 or 100 and looks at the patterns generated. So, to set up a constant to repeatedly add 10, press:
  *(any starting number)* + + 10 =
  Keep pressing the equals sign to generate the sequence, for example,
  *6 + + 10 = 16    26    36    46    56*
  and so on.

To set up a constant to repeatedly subtract 100, press:
*(any starting number)* – – 100 =
Keep pressing the equals sign to generate the sequence, for example,
*895 – – 100 = 795    695    595    495*
and so on.

**11a**

## Changing numbers by 1, 10 and 100

Write the answers.

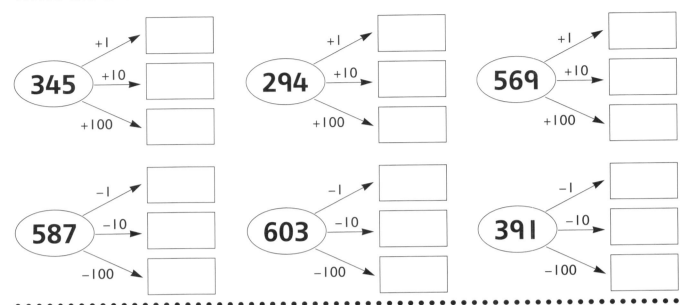

Continue these sequences.

147 148 149 ___ ___ ___ ___ ___      366 376 386 ___ ___ ___ ___ ___

404 414 424 ___ ___ ___ ___ ___      681 671 661 ___ ___ ___ ___ ___

532 522 512 ___ ___ ___ ___ ___      852 752 652 ___ ___ ___ ___ ___

397 497 597 ___ ___ ___ ___ ___      604 603 602 ___ ___ ___ ___ ___

These are parts of a 1–100 square. Write the missing numbers.

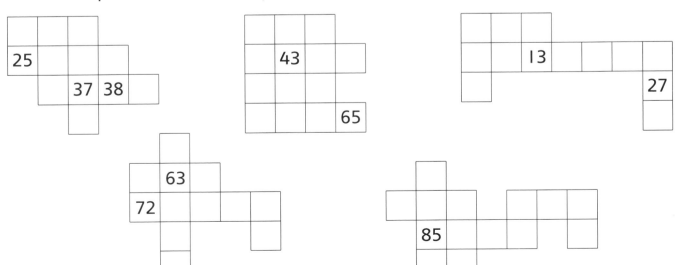

**Key Lessons in Numeracy:**
Numbers and the Number System Year 3

Name: ................................................................................................

# Changing numbers by 1, 10 and 100

A game for two players.

You need:
arrow cards
(hundreds, tens
and units)

| GAME 1 | |
|---|---|
| Number | + / − |
| | |
| | |
| | |
| | |
| | |
| | |
| | |
| | |
| | |
| | |

| GAME 2 | |
|---|---|
| Number | + / − |
| | |
| | |
| | |
| | |
| | |
| | |
| | |
| | |
| | |
| | |

| GAME 3 | |
|---|---|
| Number | + / − |
| | |
| | |
| | |
| | |
| | |
| | |
| | |
| | |
| | |
| | |

- - - - - - - - - - - - - - - - - - - - - - - - - - - - - - - - - - - - - - - - - - - - - ✂

Name: ................................................................................................

# Changing numbers by 1, 10 and 100

You need:
two dice, one
showing *more*
on three faces
and *less* on
three faces, the
other showing
*1* on two faces,
*10* on two faces
and *100* on two
faces.

| GAME 1 | | | GAME 2 | | | GAME 3 | | |
|---|---|---|---|---|---|---|---|---|
| Number | | more / less | Number | | more / less | Number | | more / less |
| 456 | + | | 456 | + | | 456 | + | |
| | − | | | − | | | − | |
| | + | | | + | | | + | |
| | − | | | − | | | − | |
| | + | | | + | | | + | |
| | − | | | − | | | − | |
| | + | | | + | | | + | |
| | − | | | − | | | − | |
| | + | | | + | | | + | |
| | − | | | − | | | − | |
| | + | | | + | | | + | |
| | − | | | − | | | − | |
| | + | | | + | | | + | |
| | − | | | − | | | − | |
| | + | | | + | | | + | |
| | − | | | − | | | − | |
| | + | | | + | | | + | |
| | − | | | − | | | − | |

**Key Lessons in Numeracy:**
Numbers and the Number System Year 3

© P. Broadbent and K.Church 1999. Heinemann Educational Ltd.
For copyright restrictions, see reverse of title page.

**Ordering 3-digit numbers**

**Lesson objective**

- to order whole numbers to at least 1000, and position them on a number line

**Language**

- order, greater than, largest

**Resources**

- large counting stick for the teacher to use (for example, a blank metre stick marked in 10 equal sections), individual fan numbers or digit cards (Resource sheets 1 and 2), **PCM12a, 12b, 12c**

**Prior learning**

- understanding place value in 3-digit numbers

**Teaching**          *whole class: about 15 minutes*

- Tell the children that this lesson is about putting different numbers in order.

- Hold up the counting stick, explaining that one end of the stick is 50, the other end is 60. Point to the middle and ask the children to name the number. Then ask for all the numbers that are smaller than 55 but greater than 50.

- Now tell the children that the values on the stick are changing – one end is 74 and the other end is 84.
  ***Where is the number 78? Point out the number 81.***
  Repeat this activity using other start and finish numbers, including hundreds, tens and units numbers.

- Using individual fan numbers or digit cards, invite six children to the front of the class and ask them to make six different numbers with the digits 2, 3 and 4. Once they have all made different possible numbers, ask them to stand in order of the sizes of numbers. Repeat this activity with six other children and a different set of digits.

**Activities**          *about 15 minutes*

**Core** (for whole class or average attainers)

- Explain to the children that they will be filling in the missing numbers on number lines in the correct order, and correcting mis-ordered numbers. Explain that the misordered numbers are in pairs, so that changing the position of each number in the pair puts both numbers in the correct order. There are at least two pairs which are in the wrong order on each line. Give them **PCM12a** and make sure they are clear about the activity.

**Extension** (for extension lesson or higher attainers)

Tell the children that they will be making as many 3-digit numbers as possible from a set of four digits. Hand out **PCM12b** and make sure they understand that they have to write the numbers in order of increasing size. Explain that they work in pairs on the second activity, each exploring the digits which their partner has chosen.

**Support** (for reinforcement lesson or lower attainers)

Give the children **PCM12c**, explaining that they will be writing sets of given numbers in the correct order. Demonstrate the activity by doing the first one with the children to make sure they understand what to do.

## Plenary       *whole class: about 10 minutes*

Ask the children to show you any 3-digit number using their fan numbers or digit cards. Encourage them to describe how they would try to find the largest number in the class. They may offer questions such as, 'Who has a number greater than 900? Any larger than 950?' and so on.

Divide the children into groups of six. Then ask them to organize themselves so that their numbers are in order. Look at each group to check they are correct.

## Further activities

- Explore personal measures. Collect, order and display a variety of personal measures, such as height, arm span, jumping distance and longest step. However, be careful to treat this activity with sensitivity.

- Collect a bag of shopping which has the weights of items shown in grams. Ask the children to put them in order. Then ask them to find and weigh objects in the classroom, and arrange them according to weight within the ordered items.

## Ordering 3-digit numbers

Look at these parts of a number line.

Fill in the missing numbers.

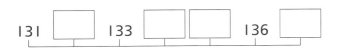

131 ☐ 133 ☐ ☐ 136 ☐

☐ ☐ 221 222 ☐ ☐ 225

☐ 507 508 ☐ ☐ ☐ ☐

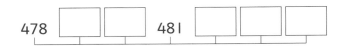

478 ☐ ☐ 481 ☐ ☐ ☐

• • • • • • • • • • • • • • • • • • • • • • • • • • • • • • • • • • • • • •

These number lines have pairs of numbers which have swapped places. Draw arrows to show the pairs. Look at the example to see how.

example:

17    20    22    18    21    19

148    152    155    151    149    153    154    150    156    157    158

364    365    366    372    368    370    369    371    367    373    374

491    492    495    494    493    496    501    498    499    500    497

609    608    607    610    611    612    616    614    615    613    617

905    898    899    900    903    902    901    904    897    906    907

**Key Lessons in Numeracy:**
Numbers and the Number System Year 3

## Ordering 3-digit numbers

6   2   8   5

Which 3-digit numbers can you make from these digits?

Write them all in order, starting with the smallest.

256

Now write your own digits.

Ask a partner to write all the numbers they can make in order.

✂ - - - - - - - - - - - - - - - - - - - - - - - - - - - - - - - - - - - - - - - - - - - - - - - - - - - - - - - - - - -

## Ordering 3-digit numbers

Write these numbers in order, starting with the smallest.

| 241 | 268 | 214 | 286 | 412 | 280 |
|---|---|---|---|---|---|

____ ____ ____ ____ ____ ____

| 196 | 194 | 201 | 197 | 200 | 191 |
|---|---|---|---|---|---|

____ ____ ____ ____ ____ ____

| 614 | 416 | 461 | 616 | 412 | 640 |
|---|---|---|---|---|---|

____ ____ ____ ____ ____ ____

| 505 | 530 | 550 | 535 | 553 | 513 |
|---|---|---|---|---|---|

____ ____ ____ ____ ____ ____

| 807 | 811 | 804 | 840 | 808 | 814 |
|---|---|---|---|---|---|

____ ____ ____ ____ ____ ____

| 754 | 457 | 547 | 744 | 705 | 474 |
|---|---|---|---|---|---|

____ ____ ____ ____ ____ ____

# LESSON 13 Comparing and ordering money

## Lesson objective

- to order amounts of money involving pounds and multiples of ten pence, using appropriate vocabulary

## Language

- between, smaller, smallest, larger, largest, greatest, least, less, most

## Resources

- sets of £1, 50p, 20p and 10p coins available for groups of about four children, individual sets of money arrow cards (Resource sheet 5), PCM13a, 13b, 13c

## Prior learning

- understanding place value in 3-digit numbers
- understanding decimal recording of money

## Teaching

### whole class: about 15 minutes

- Explain to the children that this lesson is about ordering amounts of money.

- Seat the children in mixed-ability groups of about four.
Begin by asking the whole class to:
*Start at 50p. Count on in steps of 10p to £2 and back to 50p.*
*Start at 30p. Count on in steps of 20p to £3 and back to 30p.*
*Start at 50p. Count on in steps of 50p to £5 and back to 50p.*

- Ask each group to take a handful of money and work out the total value of the coins they have. Ask a child from one group to write their group total on the board and say the amount. Ask a child from another group to do the same.
*Which is the smaller amount? Which is the larger? How do you know?*
*Which digits do you need to consider?*
Repeat the writing on the board and the comparison of the figures in pairs of groups until all the totals have been recorded. Compare four of the totals.
*Which is the smallest amount? Which is the largest? Of the remaining two, which is less?*
Record the four totals in order of decreasing size, then select and record one of the other amounts of money which is between two of the amounts already ordered.
*Between which two totals does this go?*
Ask a child to draw an arrow from this total to its position in the order. Repeat until all the totals have been ordered.

For example, we have £2.50, £1.20, 55p, 25p and you must place 30p correctly.

£2·50        £1·20        55p        30p        25p

### Core (for whole class or average attainers)

Explain to the children that they will be working out total amounts of money and writing them in order of size. Give them **PCM13a** and tell them that they can use the coins on the table to help them work out the amounts if they wish. Remind the children that when two amounts have the same number of pounds, they must look at the pence to decide which is the greater amount.

### Extension (for extension lesson or higher attainers)

Give the children **PCM13b**, explaining that they will be ordering the prices of various items from different price lists. Point out that the price lists show how much different shops charge for the same goods, each list being a different pet shop. The children should find the lowest price for each item first, then the next lowest, and so on until they have put the prices for each item in order. Finally, they should work out how much the shopping basket would cost if they bought each item at the cheapest prices and how much if they bought each item at the most expensive prices.

### Support (for reinforcement lesson or lower attainers)

Ask each child to take a few coins and work out the total value. Then, in pairs, compare the two amounts and decide which is the larger and which is smaller. Ask each pair to describe to the rest of the group what they have done and use this opportunity to help any children who are having difficulties. Tell the children that this activity involves putting different amounts of money in order of value, starting from the smallest. Remind them that they need to look at the pounds first, and then at the pence if the two amounts have the same number of pounds. They can use real coins to help them if they wish. Give the children **PCM13c** and go through the activity with them. Stay with them as they complete it to make sure they include all the amounts.

Say two amounts of money. Encourage the children to use their money arrow cards to show you a different amount which is between those two amounts. Discuss the different amounts using appropriate language. Repeat this using different ranges of money.

Explain that they have been learning how to order amounts of money, which is what adults do when they compare prices when shopping.

### Further activities

- Provide some mail order catalogues and ask the children to find the same type of items, perhaps various trainers, at different costs. Display these in order of price. Then carry out a class survey to compare the various prices – what is the greatest difference in price and what is the least?

Name: ........................................................................................

## Comparing and ordering money

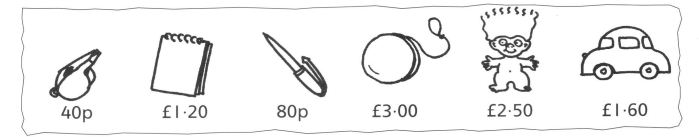

| | | | | | |
|---|---|---|---|---|---|
| 40p | £1·20 | 80p | £3·00 | £2·50 | £1·60 |

These six children have bought different items from this shop.
Work out how much each has spent.

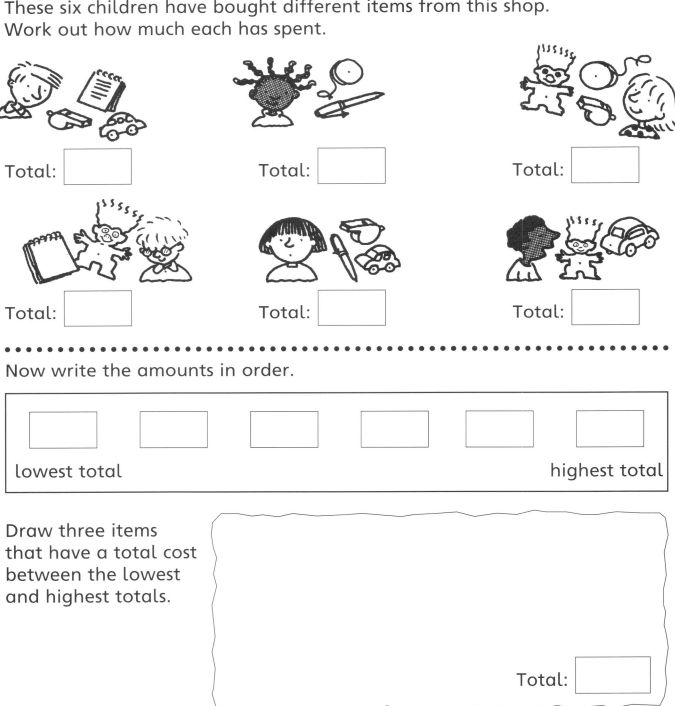

Total: ☐        Total: ☐        Total: ☐

Total: ☐        Total: ☐        Total: ☐

• • • • • • • • • • • • • • • • • • • • • • • • • • • • • • • • • • • • •

Now write the amounts in order.

| ☐ | ☐ | ☐ | ☐ | ☐ | ☐ |
|---|---|---|---|---|---|
| lowest total | | | | | highest total |

Draw three items
that have a total cost
between the lowest
and highest totals.

Total: ☐

**Key Lessons in Numeracy:**
Numbers and the Number System Year 3

Name: ..............................................................................................

## Comparing and ordering money

Look at and compare these price lists from 4 different shops.

| Shop A | | Shop B | | Shop C | | Shop D | |
|---|---|---|---|---|---|---|---|
| rubber bone | 90p | dog collar | £1·60 | brush | £1·90 | dog collar | £1·90 |
| dog collar | £2·10 | rubber bone | £1·20 | food bowl | £1·40 | food bowl | £2·60 |
| brush | £1·60 | food bowl | £1·30 | dog collar | £1·90 | brush | £2·10 |
| food bowl | £1·70 | brush | £2·40 | rubber bone | £1·10 | rubber bone | 80p |
| Total: | | Total: | | Total: | | Total: | |

|  | lowest cost | | highest cost | |
|---|---|---|---|---|
| rubber bone | _____ | _____ | _____ | _____ |
| dog collar | _____ | _____ | _____ | _____ |
| brush | _____ | _____ | _____ | _____ |
| food bowl | _____ | _____ | _____ | _____ |

|  | Total |
|---|---|
| lowest cost | _____ |
| highest cost | _____ |

✂ - - - - - - - - - - - - - - - - - - - - - - - - - - - - - - - - - - - - - - - - - - - - - - - - - - - - - - - - - - - - - - - - -

Name: ..............................................................................................

## Comparing and ordering money

Write these prices in order of size, starting with the smallest.

£1·80 £2·10 £2·20 £1·50 80p

£2·50 £3·70 £3·50 £3·00 £2·60

_____ _____ _____ _____ _____

90p £1·70 £1·80 £1·00 £1·10

£4·20 £4·00 £3·80 £3·90 £3·60

_____ _____ _____ _____ _____

**Key Lessons in Numeracy:**
Numbers and the Number System Year 3

# Estimating and rounding

**Estimating objects**

## Lesson objective

- to read and begin to write the vocabulary of estimation and approximation, and to give a sensible estimate of up to 100 objects

## Language

- estimate, roughly, approximation

## Resources

- counting stick, individual sets of fan numbers or digit cards (Resource sheets 1 and 2), a transparent jar or container with approximately 100 objects inside (for example, cubes, beads, marbles, sweets and nuts), six further containers (with 20, 20, 30, 40, 50 and 100 of the same objects inside and lettered A–F but not in order of size), **PCM14a, 14b, 14c**

## Prior learning

- estimating up to 50 objects

**Teaching**    *whole class: about 15 minutes*

- Explain to the children that this lesson is about estimating numbers of objects and noting their position on a number line.

- *What does 'estimate' mean?*
  Discuss the responses offered and emphasize that estimating involves more than guessing – an estimate is based on something we know and is nearly accurate.

- Hold up a blank counting stick and name one end 0 and the other 10. Point to a position between these two points and ask the children to estimate the number. Repeat this activity with other positions. Then change the ranges to, say, 0 to 20, 30 to 40, 0 to 100, and so on.

- Ask the children to respond to the following questions, showing the answers numerically using their fan numbers or digit cards.
  *How many children are there in the class? So about how many children do you think are in two classes in the school? How did you make your estimate? Roughly how many children are there in three classes? How did you make your estimate?*
  *How many books do you think there are on that shelf? How did you make your estimate?*
  If the estimates are based on guesses, ask if the children can think of a way to make the estimate more accurate without counting.
  *So roughly how many books are there on three shelves?*

- Show the children the container of 100 objects.
  *About how many [cubes] do you think there are in this jar? How did you make your estimate? How could we make the estimate more accurate?*
  Discuss the suggestions offered and try one or two out. Then tell the children that there are about 100 [cubes] in the jar. Discuss the accuracy of the estimates.

**Key Lessons in Numeracy:** Numbers and the Number System Year 3

**Activities**                    *about 20 minutes*

### Core (for whole class or average attainers)

Explain to the children that they will be making estimates of positions on number lines. Hand out **PCM14a** and tell them that the arrows on the number lines are pointing to a number which they have to estimate. Point out that each number line is different, and that the numbers at each end of the lines show the range. In the second part of the activity, the children are to draw arrows from two sets of given numbers to show their estimates of where the numbers are on the lines.

### Extension (for extension lesson or higher attainers)

Discuss with the children the type of estimates we make in everyday life, such as the number of bricks needed to build a wall, the number of pencils the school needs for a year or the number of parents who might attend sports day. Ask the children to work in pairs and give them **PCM14b**. Each pair should select something you have discussed, or one of the items listed on the **PCM**, and think carefully about how they could estimate the number. They should record their method on the sheet before using it to make an estimate. Finally, they should record the estimate and comment on how accurate they think it will be. Can they think of a way to check the accuracy of the estimate?

### Support (for reinforcement lesson or lower attainers)

Explain to the group that they will be working together to estimate the number of objects in a variety of containers. Hand out **PCM14c** and give them containers A–F. Tell them that after each estimate they should count the objects to see how accurate their estimate was before going on to the next container. This will help them to make their next estimate more accurate.

**Plenary**                    *whole class: about 5 minutes*

Ask the children who did the 'Core' activity to describe to the class how they made their estimates of the numbers on the number lines. Ask the children who completed the 'Extension' and 'Support' activities to explain the methods they used to estimate a number and to discuss the different methods used.

Explain that adults use estimation when they don't need to know an exact figure and a rough idea will do. Give some examples of such situations and ask the children to suggest others. You might suggest the number of potatoes needed for a meal; the length of a journey when considering what time arrival might be; the amount of money we need to take on a day out.

### Further activities

- Provide some copies of pages from the children's reading books to investigate the words.
  *Which is the most common word? How could you use estimation to find out?*

- Develop this investigation by considering the most common single letter on a page and use estimation to find the most common letter in the book.

Name: ...................................................................................

14a

## Estimating objects

Estimate the numbers these arrows point to.

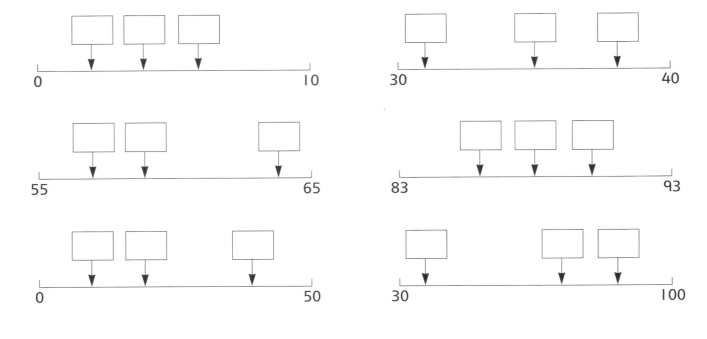

. . . . . . . . . . . . . . . . . . . . . . . . . . . . . . . . . . . . . . . . . . . . . . . . . . . .

Write these numbers on each number line.

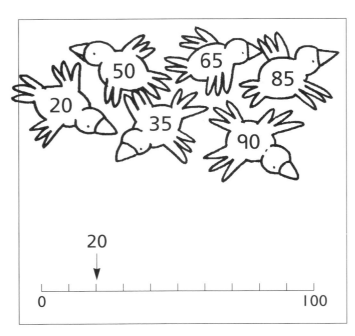

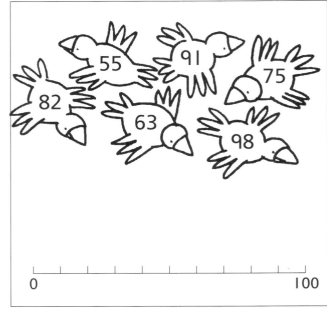

Name: ...........................................................................................

## Estimating objects

Could you give an accurate estimate for any of these?

The number of pencils the school needs for a year.

The number of words on a page in your reading book.

The number of sandwiches eaten in school in a week.

The number of bricks in a wall.

The number of beans in a beanbag.

The number of books in the bookcase.

Choose one.
How could you estimate the number?
Record your method and your estimate here.

Estimate [ ]

- - - - - - - - - - - - - - - - - - - - - - - - - - - - - - - - - - - - - - - - - - - - - - ✂

Name: ...........................................................................................

## Estimating objects

You need: six containers with small objects inside

Estimate how many objects are in each container.

Then count them to check your estimate.

| Container | A | B | C | D | E | F |
|---|---|---|---|---|---|---|
| Estimate | | | | | | |
| Actual number | | | | | | |

**Key Lessons in Numeracy:**
Numbers and the Number System Year 3

# Rounding numbers

## Lesson objective

- to round any 2-digit number to the nearest 10 and any 3-digit number to the nearest 100

## Language

- round, rounded, nearest, closer to, approximate, approximation

## Resources

- class number line, individual fan numbers or digit cards (Resource sheets 1 and 2), clock, **PCM15a, 15b, 15c**

## Prior learning

- beginning to round to the nearest 10

## Teaching

### whole class: about 15 minutes

- Explain to the children that this lesson is about rounding numbers to the nearest 10 and to the nearest 100.

- Point to a number such as 32 on the number line and ask whether it is closer to 30 or 40. Repeat this activity for different numbers, but avoid those which have 5 as a units digit. Explain that what the children have been doing is called *rounding* numbers to the nearest 10. Some numbers are rounded up to the next 10 and some are rounded down to the previous 10.

  *What about the numbers which are halfway between two tens? Can anyone remember the rule we use to tell us whether to round a number up or down?*

  Make sure the children are clear that such numbers are rounded up.

- Remove the number line. Say some numbers, including those with five units. Ask the class to round these numbers to the nearest 10 and to show you that number on their fan numbers or digit cards.

  *What does 'rounding' mean?*

  Discuss the responses, emphasizing that we use rounding when we need an approximate number, rather than an exact number, and this usually involves larger numbers.

- Explain that we can round 3-digit numbers up or down to the nearest 100 in a similar way, but instead of looking at the units digit as we do when rounding to the nearest 10, we have to look at the tens digit. Write a number such as 320 on the board and ask whether it is nearer to 300 or 400. Repeat this using different 3-digit numbers, including those which have units, focusing the children's attention on the tens digit in each case.

- *What about 450? It is half-way between two hundreds, so should we round it up or down?*

  Discuss the responses, emphasizing the rule that 'half-way' numbers are always rounded up.

## Activities

### about 15 minutes

**Core** (for whole class or average attainers)

Give the children **PCM15a** and tell them that they will be rounding numbers to the nearest 10 or the nearest 100.

**Extension** (for extension lesson or higher attainers)

Explain to the children that this activity involves rounding distances between cities to the nearest 10km. Hand out **PCM15b**. Before they begin, provide some examples to demonstrate how to read the distance table to make sure they understand the how it works.

**Support** (for reinforcement lesson or lower attainers)

Repeat some of the oral activities done in the first part of the lesson involving rounding numbers to the nearest 10 and ensure that the children understand the process. Give them **PCM15c**, telling them that they will be rounding numbers to the nearest 10.

## Plenary — *whole class: about 10 minutes*

Have a clock clearly visible. Ask the children to tell you the time to the nearest hour, then to the nearest 5 minutes.

Measure a child's height with a measuring stick and tell the children the exact measurement. Ask them what the height is to the nearest 10 centimetres, then to the nearest metre. Remind them that this is an approximate height.

Ask if anyone knows how far it is from your school to the village or town. If they need encouragement, provide them with the actual distance before asking them to round up or down for an approximation.

*What is the rule for rounding numbers to the nearest 10? What about rounding to the nearest 100?*

Explain that we often approximate in real life by rounding numbers and measures up or down when we don't need a precise number.

## Further activities

- Ask the children to measure the dimensions of the classroom. Then, using a scale of 50cm:1cm, draw its floor plan on squared paper by rounding lengths to the nearest metre and half metre.

- Develop this idea by drawing plans of other classrooms and putting them together to show an approximate plan of the school (or one floor, if it is multi-storeyed).

## Rounding numbers

Round these numbers to the nearest 10.
Draw a circle around your choice.

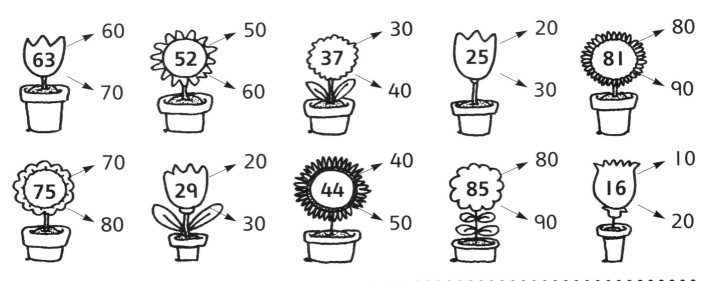

Round these numbers to the nearest 100.

340 → ☐          230 → ☐          560 → ☐          850 → ☐

271 → ☐          649 → ☐          452 → ☐          939 → ☐

Round each of these weights to the nearest 100g.

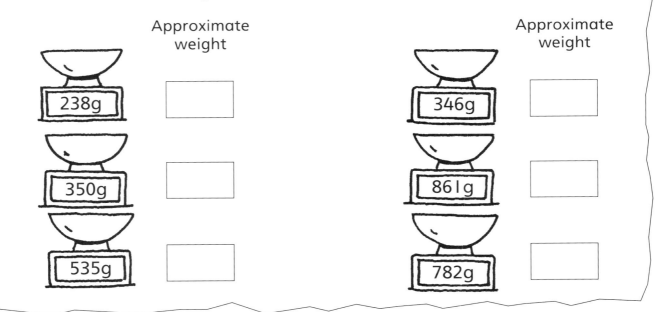

## Rounding numbers

This table shows the distances in kilometres between different cities.

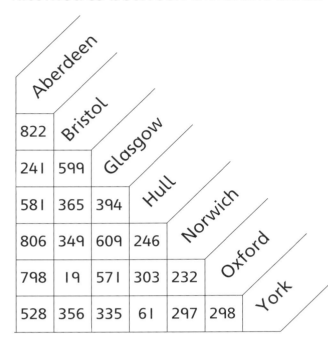

| | | | | | | | |
|---|---|---|---|---|---|---|---|
| Aberdeen | | | | | | | |
| 822 | Bristol | | | | | | |
| 241 | 599 | Glasgow | | | | | |
| 581 | 365 | 394 | Hull | | | | |
| 806 | 349 | 609 | 246 | Norwich | | | |
| 798 | 19 | 571 | 303 | 232 | Oxford | | |
| 528 | 356 | 335 | 61 | 297 | 298 | York | |

To the nearest 10km, what is the distance between these cities?

1. Glasgow → Aberdeen [      ] km
2. Bristol → Oxford [      ] km
3. York → Norwich [      ] km
4. Hull → Bristol [      ] km
5. Norwich → Glasgow [      ] km
6. Hull → York [      ] km
7. Oxford → Norwich [      ] km
8. York → Glasgow [      ] km

Which two cities are approximately 600km apart?

[                    ] and [                    ]

---

## Rounding numbers

Round these numbers to the nearest 10.
Draw a circle around your choice on the number line.

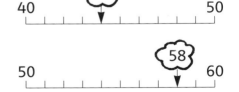
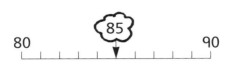
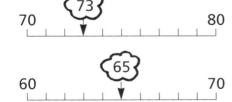

Round these numbers to the nearest 10.

34 → [      ]      82 → [      ]      25 → [      ]      16 → [      ]

72 → [      ]      91 → [      ]      39 → [      ]      45 → [      ]

**Key Lessons in Numeracy:**
Numbers and the Number System Year 3

# Fractions

**Recognizing unit fractions**

## Lesson objective

- to recognize unit fractions such as $\frac{1}{2}, \frac{1}{3}, \frac{1}{4}, \frac{1}{5}, \frac{1}{10}$ and use them to find fractions of shapes

## Language

- fraction, one half, one quarter, one third, one tenth, whole, part, equal parts

## Resources

- A5 pieces of paper, shapes drawn on the board showing thirds and tenths, **PCM16a, 16b, 16c**

## Prior learning

- recognition of one half and one quarter of shapes

---

**Teaching**    *whole class: about 20 minutes*

- Explain to the children that this lesson is about finding and making fractions of shapes. Begin by asking if they can remember what a fraction is. Ensure they understand that it concerns equal parts of a whole. Many children have difficulty with the word *fraction* even when they understand the concept. Make sure that you use the word repeatedly during the lesson, asking questions such as 'What fraction can you see?' and 'What fraction is left?'

- Give each child a piece of A5 paper. Tell them to fold their piece of paper exactly in half. Ask them to look carefully and make sure that each part is equal.
  *How many halves make one whole?*
  Now tell them to fold their paper exactly into quarters, again very carefully.
  *How many quarters make one whole? How many quarters make one half? If I cover up one quarter how many quarters can I see? What do we call the fraction which is half of one half?*

- Write the fractions $\frac{1}{2}$ and $\frac{1}{4}$ on the board. Remind the children that the bottom number tells us how many equal parts the whole has been divided into. So 2 below the line means that there are 2 equal parts.
  *What does 4 below the line mean?*

- Draw a rectangle on the board and divide it equally into thirds. Point to one third.
  *What fraction of the whole rectangle is this? What fraction is the rest? How many thirds make a whole?*
  Draw a different shape on the board and divide it equally into thirds. Repeat the questions, as above. Write $\frac{1}{3}$ the board and ask the children what it means.

- Draw a rectangle on the board which has been divided equally into tenths. Establish that it has 10 equal parts.
  *What fraction of the rectangle is one of the parts? Can anyone write one tenth on the board? What fraction of the whole shape is two of the parts?*
  Ask questions like these for other tenths.
  Repeat this with a shape showing fifths.
  Finally, point out the fractions $\frac{1}{2}, \frac{1}{3}, \frac{1}{4}, \frac{1}{10}$ written on the board and ask what each fraction means.

## Activities — *about 15 minutes*

### Core (for whole class or average attainers)

Explain to the children that they will be colouring fractions of different shapes and recognizing the fractions of pre-shaded shapes. Hand out **PCM16a** and ask them to complete it.

### Extension (for extension lesson or higher attainers)

Give the children **PCM16b**. Tell them that one third of each pattern needs colouring, but they all need to be different. Ask them how they think they can be sure to have all the different combinations, encouraging them to be systematic.

### Support (for reinforcement lesson or lower attainers)

Give each child a copy of **PCM16c** and look at the row of rectangles together. Ask them to colour half of the first rectangle, to colour one third of the next, and finally one quarter of the last rectangle. Explain that they will be colouring fractions of the other shapes in a similar way according to the instructions. Make sure they can read the fractions before they continue.

## Plenary — *whole class: about 5 minutes*

Look again at the rectangle divided into tenths on the board. Shade in five tenths.

***What fraction of the shape is shaded? Is there a different fraction for this part of the shape?***

Discuss the fact it also represents one half.

***How many tenths are the same as one half? How many tenths are the same as two halves?***

Write $\frac{1}{3}$ on the board and ask what fraction you have written. Repeat this for $\frac{1}{2}$, $\frac{1}{4}$, $\frac{1}{5}$ and $\frac{1}{10}$.

### Further activities

- Give each child a rectangle divided into eighths. Ask them to use it to design different flags according to given criteria, for example:
  ***Make half the flag red, one quarter of it yellow, one eighth of it green and keep one eighth white.***

- Develop this activity by this time giving the children a rectangle divided into twelfths, and including halves, thirds and sixths in the criteria.

Name: ....................................................................................  16a

## Recognizing unit fractions

You need: blue, red and yellow pencils

Colour $\frac{1}{2}$ of each shape blue.

 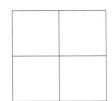 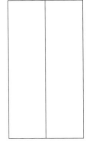 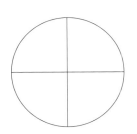 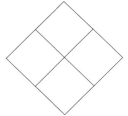

Colour $\frac{1}{3}$ of each shape red.

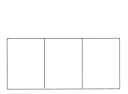 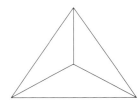  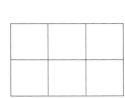 

Colour $\frac{1}{4}$ of each shape yellow.

  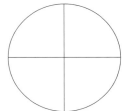 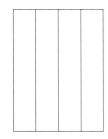 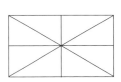

Tick the shapes which have $\frac{1}{3}$ shaded.

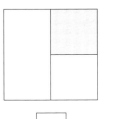  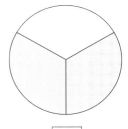 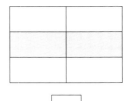

   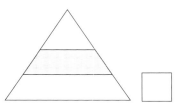

**Key Lessons in Numeracy:**
Numbers and the Number System Year 3

Name: ............................................................................................

16b

## Recognizing unit fractions

Colour in $\frac{1}{3}$ of each of these shapes.
Make sure each is coloured in a different pattern.

 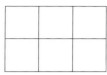 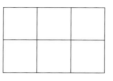 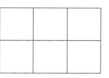 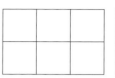 

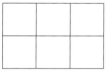  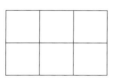 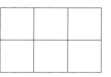 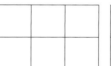 

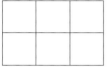 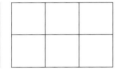 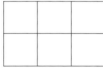

How many
different patterns
would there be
if you coloured in $\frac{2}{3}$?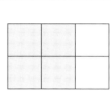

---

Name: ............................................................................................

16c

## Recognizing unit fractions

You need: blue, red and yellow pencils

Colour $\frac{1}{2}$.     Colour $\frac{1}{3}$. 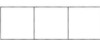    Colour $\frac{1}{4}$.

Colour $\frac{1}{2}$ of each shape red.

Colour $\frac{1}{4}$ of each shape blue.

Colour $\frac{1}{3}$ of each shape yellow.

 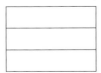 

Divide this shape
into thirds.

**Key Lessons in Numeracy:**
Numbers and the Number System Year 3

**Fractions of numbers**

### Lesson objective

- to recognize and name fractions such as $\frac{1}{2}$, $\frac{1}{3}$, $\frac{1}{4}$, $\frac{1}{5}$, $\frac{1}{10}$, and use them to find fractions of numbers

### Language

- fraction, one half, one quarter, one third, one fifth, one tenth, divided by

### Resources

- 4 × 4 square drawn on 2cm squared paper, displayed so that all the children can see it, individual fan numbers or digit cards (Resource sheets 1 and 2), **PCM17a, 17b, 17c**

### Prior learning

- finding one half and one quarter of small numbers of objects

---

**Teaching**  *whole class: about 20 minutes*

- Explain to the children that this lesson is about finding fractions of numbers. As an introduction, begin by asking:

  *What is half of 8? What is half of 20?*

  Repeat this using a few other numbers which the children can work out mentally and ask them to show you the answers using their fan numbers or digit cards.

  *How do you work out what half of a number is?*

  Establish that the number is divided by 2. Write $\frac{1}{2}$ on the board and remind the children that the bottom number shows how many equal parts the whole is divided into.

- Look at the prepared *4 × 4* square. Draw lines on the square to show quarters.

  *What fraction of the whole shape is one of the parts? How many small squares are there in the whole shape? How many small squares are there in each quarter? So what is one quarter of 16?*

- Write $\frac{1}{4}$ on the board.

  *How could we find one quarter of a number without drawing a shape?*

  Establish that the number would be divided by 4 because the 4 below the line tells us to do that. Ask them to show you one quarter of a few multiples of 4 using their fan numbers or digit cards.

- Write $\frac{1}{3}$ on the board.

  *How could we find one third of a number without drawing a shape?*

  Establish that the number would be divided by 3 because the 3 below the line tells us to do that. Ask them to show you one third of a few multiples of 3 using their fan numbers or digit cards.

- Write $\frac{1}{10}$ on the board.

  *How could we find one tenth of a number without drawing a shape?*

  Establish that the number would be divided by 10 because the 10 below the line tells us to do that. Ask them to show you one tenth of a few multiples of 10 using their fan numbers or digit cards.

- Write $\frac{1}{5}$ on the board.

  *How could we find one fifth of a number?*

  Establish that the number would be divided by 5 because the 5 below the line indicates that. Ask the children to show you one fifth of a few multiples of 5 using their fan numbers or digit cards.

*about 15 minutes*

### Core (for whole class or average attainers)

Give the children **PCM17a**, explaining that they will be colouring shapes and finding fractions of different numbers, finding further fractions of numbers without shapes and making a fraction pattern.

### Extension (for extension lesson or higher attainers)

Tell the children that this activity involves finding fractions of different starting numbers. Hand out **PCM17b**, making sure they understand how to find the missing numbers. Ensure that when they reach the part where they choose their own starting number, they choose numbers which work with the fractions given.

### Support (for reinforcement lesson or lower attainers)

Give each child a copy of **PCM17c** and look at the 12-square rectangle together. First, ask the children to say how many squares it covers, then to draw lines on the rectangle to show quarters. Can they tell you how many squares there are in one quarter of the rectangle? Emphasize that they are counting the squares in one of the quarters only, before you link this to the calculation $\frac{1}{4}$ of 12. Explain that they will be carrying out the same activity but using different fractions and different shapes. Before they complete the **PCM**, make sure they can read the fractions.

**Plenary** *whole class: about 5 minutes*

Ask the children some questions which involve finding fractions of numbers in contexts, for example:

*There are 30 children in the class.*
*Half of them walk to school. How many children walk to school?*

*One tenth of the children cycle to school. How many children cycle?*

*One third of the children come by car. How many children come by car?*

*There are 24 beads in a bag.*
*One quarter of the beads are red. How many red beads are there?*

*One third of the beads are blue. How many blue beads are there?*

Ask the children to tell you the rule for finding fractions of numbers, reminding them about the number below the line in a fraction.

### Further activities

- Provide the children with some realistic problems involving fractions of quantities.
  *One third of the bus is empty. There are 72 seats altogether. How many seats are empty?*
  $\frac{1}{4}$ *of the pencils need sharpening.*
  *If there are 36 pencils altogether, how many need sharpening?*

- Investigate numbers which can be divided into different fractions, for example, 12 can be divided into half, a quarter, a third and a twelfth.
  *Which numbers can you find which can be divided into four or more fractions?*

Name: ...................................................................................

## Fractions of numbers

Colour the squares to make a pattern.
Only colour the fractions given.
Then write the answers to the problems.

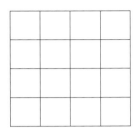

$\frac{1}{2}$ of 16 = _____

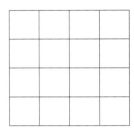

$\frac{1}{4}$ of 16 = _____

$\frac{1}{5}$ of 10 = _____

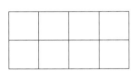

$\frac{1}{4}$ of 8 = _____

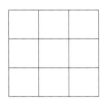

$\frac{1}{3}$ of 9 = _____

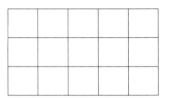

$\frac{1}{5}$ of 15 = _____

Write the answers.

$\frac{1}{4}$ of 16 = _____   $\frac{1}{2}$ of 14 = _____   $\frac{1}{3}$ of 6 = _____

$\frac{1}{3}$ of 18 = _____   $\frac{1}{10}$ of 30 = _____   $\frac{1}{5}$ of 20 = _____

$\frac{1}{10}$ of 80 = _____   $\frac{1}{4}$ of 24 = _____   $\frac{1}{5}$ of 35 = _____

Make a pattern on this grid using these fractions of colour.

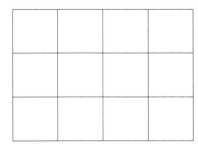

$\frac{1}{2}$ red        $\frac{1}{6}$ green

$\frac{1}{4}$ yellow        $\frac{1}{12}$ orange

Key Lessons in Numeracy:
Numbers and the Number System Year 3

Name: ..........................................................................................................

## Fractions of numbers

Write the fractions of these numbers.    Write the missing numbers.

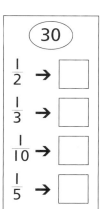
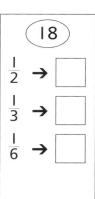
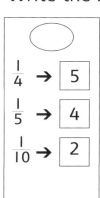
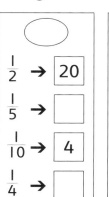
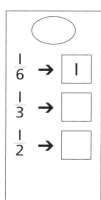

Now choose your own starting number.
Be careful with the numbers you choose.

- - - - - - - - - - - - - - - - - - - - - - - - - - - - - - - - - - - - - - - - - - - - - - - - - - - - - - - ✂

Name: ..........................................................................................................

## Fractions of numbers

Colour in the fractions. Fill in the answers.

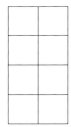
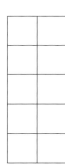

$\frac{1}{4}$ of 12 = _____     $\frac{1}{2}$ of 6 = _____     $\frac{1}{4}$ of 8 = _____     $\frac{1}{2}$ of 10 = _____

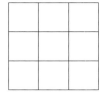

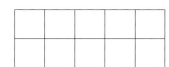

$\frac{1}{3}$ of 9 = _____     $\frac{1}{3}$ of 6 = _____     $\frac{1}{2}$ of 4 = _____     $\frac{1}{2}$ of 10 = _____

**Key Lessons in Numeracy:**
Numbers and the Number System Year 3

## Lesson objective

- to recognize simple fractions that are several parts of a whole, such as $\frac{3}{4}$, $\frac{2}{3}$ or $\frac{3}{10}$

## Language

- fraction, one half, one quarter, three quarters, one third, two thirds, one tenth, three tenths, and so on

## Resources

- two strips of thin card per child, counting stick, Multilink cubes, **PCM18a, 18b, 18c**

## Prior learning

- recognizing unit fractions, such as halves, quarters, thirds, and so on

**Teaching**     *whole class: about 20 minutes*

- Explain to the children that this lesson is about fractions of different sizes. Make sure they remember that a fraction concerns equal parts of a whole.

- Provide each child with two strips of thin card. Ask them to fold their first strip in half, then in half again to make four quarters.
  *What fraction of the whole strip is one of the four equal parts? Show me one quarter of your strip by folding it up. What fraction of the whole strip is two of the four equal parts?*
  If the response is 'one half', ask if they can suggest a different fraction that it also equals.
  *Which is the bigger fraction, one quarter or two quarters?*
  *What fraction of the whole strip is three of the four equal parts?*
  *Which is the bigger fraction, three quarters or two quarters? Show me four quarters. What is this equal to?*
  Make sure the children appreciate $\frac{4}{4}$ is one whole.

- Now ask the children to fold the second strip of card, but this time into thirds.
  *Show me one third of your strip. Show me two thirds. Show me the whole strip. How many thirds is this?*
  With both strips in front of them, ask the children to show different fractions by choosing and folding one of the strips. For example,
  *Show me two quarters, three thirds, one quarter, half, three quarters.*

- Hold up a counting stick, naming one end 0 and the other end 1. Explain that the stick is in 10 sections, with each section showing one tenth. Point to each section one by one, counting up in tenths: $\frac{1}{10}$, $\frac{2}{10}$, $\frac{3}{10}$, $\frac{4}{10}$ and so on, and write the fractions on the board. Ask if they know what $\frac{5}{10}$ is equal to. Point to random positions, asking the children to name the fractions, including the equivalent fractions.

- Write the fractions $\frac{1}{4}$, $\frac{3}{4}$, $\frac{1}{3}$ and $\frac{2}{3}$ on the board. Remind the children that the bottom number tells us how many equal parts the whole has been divided into. So 4 below the line means that there are 4 equal parts. The top number shows how many of these parts are taken.

**Activities**     *about 15 minutes*

**Core** (for whole class or average attainers)

Give the children **PCM18a**, explaining that they will be making and colouring specified fractions in different shapes.

**Extension** (for extension lesson or higher attainers)

Give the children **PCM18b**. Point out that they have been given only the quarter and third parts of whole shapes. Make sure they realize that there could be a variety of whole shapes and that they need to check each one as they complete them for accuracy. Note that the children's shapes may all be different.

**Support** (for reinforcement lesson or lower attainers)

Hand out **PCM18c** and look at the top rectangle together. Repeat the oral activities about tenths from earlier in the lesson. Ask the children to colour one tenth of the rectangle in one colour, two tenths in a second colour and, finally, five tenths in a third colour. How many tenths are left? Explain that they will be colouring fractions of the other shapes in a similar way according to the instructions. Make sure they can read the fractions before they begin.

**Plenary**      *whole class: about 5 minutes*

Write $\frac{3}{10}$ on the board and ask what fraction you have written.

*What does the 10 mean? What about the 3?*

Repeat this activity by writing other tenths, quarters and thirds on the board. Use Multilink cubes to illustrate fractions of a whole. Hold up 4 cubes joined together. Explain that this is a 'whole' shape.

*Who can show one quarter of the shape?*

Ask a volunteer to demonstrate.

*Who can show three quarters?*

**Further activities**

- Give each child a *6 × 4* piece of 2 cm squared paper so that each child has 24 squares. Ask them fold the grid to show you half of the grid, one quarter of the grid, three quarters, one third, two thirds, and so on.

- Develop this activity by asking questions relating to 24 hours in a day such as:
*If I sleep for one third of the time, what fraction of the day am I awake? How many hours does this make?*
*If I am in the house for three quarters of the day, how many hours am I away from the house?*

## Non-unitary fractions

You need: red, blue, green and yellow pencils

Colour $\frac{1}{4}$ of each shape red.      Colour $\frac{3}{4}$ of each shape blue.

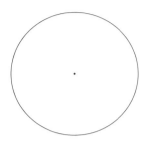

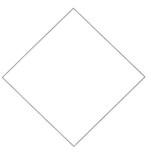

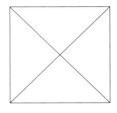
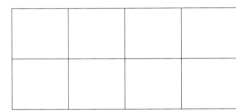

Colour $\frac{1}{3}$ of each shape green.      Colour $\frac{2}{3}$ of each shape yellow.

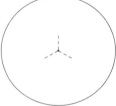

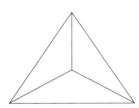

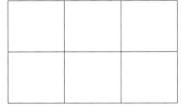

Colour $\frac{3}{10}$ of this shape red.

Colour $\frac{2}{10}$ yellow.

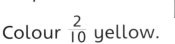

What fraction is left?

## Non-unitary fractions

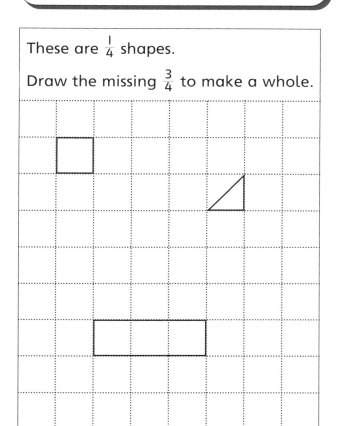

These are $\frac{1}{4}$ shapes.

Draw the missing $\frac{3}{4}$ to make a whole.

These are $\frac{1}{3}$ shapes.

Draw the missing $\frac{2}{3}$ to make a whole.

- - - - - - - - - - - - - - - - - - - - - - - - - - - - - - - - - - - - - - - - ✂

## Non-unitary fractions

You need: green, yellow and red pencils

Colour $\frac{1}{10}$ in green, $\frac{2}{10}$ in yellow and $\frac{5}{10}$ in red.

Colour $\frac{3}{4}$ of each shape green.

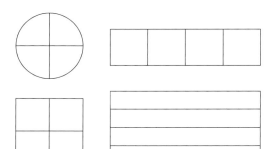

Colour $\frac{2}{3}$ of each shape red.

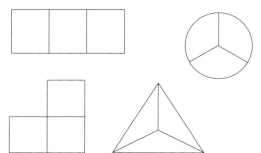

**Recognizing equivalent fractions**

### Lesson objective

- to recognize simple equivalent fractions

### Language

- fraction, one half, one quarter, two quarters, three quarters, four quarters, one tenth, two tenths, equal to, equivalent

### Resources

- a transparent bag containing 8 objects (for example, beads or cubes), a large copy of the equivalent fractions wall at the top of **PCM19a** displayed so that all the children can see it, **PCM19a, 19b, 19c**

### Prior learning

- understanding halves, quarters and tenths
- finding fractions of shapes and numbers

**Teaching**     *whole class: about 20 minutes*

- Explain to the children that this lesson is about finding fractions which have the same value as other fractions.

- Hold up the bag containing the objects, showing the children that there are eight in the bag.

  *If I give one quarter of them to [John], how many beads will [he] have?*

  Give two beads to the child.

  *If I give one quarter of them to [Sonia], how many beads will [she] have?*

  Give two beads to the child.

  *How many beads did I have to start with? So how many beads do I have left? How many beads do [John] and [Sonia] have between them? Why is that the same as the number left in the bag? What fraction of the beads do I have left?*

  *What is half of 8? What is quarter of 8? What are two quarters of 8?*

  *So what other fraction is equal to two quarters?*

  Write $\frac{1}{2} = \frac{2}{4}$ on the board. Explain that when two fractions are equal to each other, we call them *equivalent fractions*.

- Show the children the large fraction wall. Explain that the top strip represents one whole, and the line below is divided to represent the halves of the whole.

  *How many halves make one whole?*

  Point to the next strip of the diagram representing quarters.

  *What fraction of the whole do each of these parts represent? How many quarters are equal to one whole? How many quarters are equivalent to half? If I have three quarters, what fraction do I need to make one whole?*

  Point to the next strip of the diagram and count the equal parts together. Establish that there are five in total.

  *What fraction of the whole do these represent? How many fifths are equal to one whole?*

  Discuss the last strip of tenths.

  *How many tenths are equal to one whole? How many tenths are equivalent to half?*

  *If I have 8 tenths, what fraction do I need to make one whole?*

  *If I have 6 tenths, what fraction do I need to make one whole?*

  *If I have 7 tenths, what fraction do I need to make one whole?*

  *If I have 5 tenths, what fraction do I need to make one whole? What other fraction could I use?*

*about 15 minutes*

## Core (for whole class or average attainers)

Tell the children that they will be finding and making equivalent fractions. Give them **PCM19a** and make sure they understand each section.

## Extension (for extension lesson or higher attainers)

Hand out **PCM19b**. Make sure the children understand they will be colouring each half of different shapes in different colours or patterns. They then work out the fractions equivalent to half.

## Support (for reinforcement lesson or lower attainers)

Give the children **PCM19c** and work through the first part of this together. Look at rectangle 1. Ask the children to draw a vertical line on the rectangle to show halves.

Then ask them to draw a vertical line on rectangle 2 to show quarters. Still working on rectangle 2, tell the children they are going to colour in 2 quarters. Make sure they colour in the quarters relative to the halves on rectangle 1. Establish that the 2 quarters are equal to the half.

Look at rectangle 3, ask them to draw a vertical line, as before, making sure the children understand that it has been divided into 10 equal parts. Ask what fraction of the rectangle each division is, ensuring they understand each is one tenth. Tell them to shade the 5 tenths which are relative to one of the halves on rectangle 1. Establish that the 5 tenths are equal to one half.

Allow the children time to complete the second half of the activity.

**Plenary**   *whole class: about 5 minutes*

Draw a picture of a cake on the board. Work through the sentences below and mark the fractions on the cake as you go:

*If I have a cake and cut it in half, then cut one of the halves in half again, what fraction of the cake will one of the small pieces be? If I give one of the small pieces to [Maria] and the other to [Raj] who will have more cake? If I cut the other half into 5 equal parts, what fraction of the whole cake will each part be? If I gave 2 of those pieces to [Shane] what fraction of the whole cake would [he] have? Would [he] have the same amount of cake as the other two children? Would [he] have more or less than they have? What if I give [him] 3 pieces?*

Then ask:

*What fraction is equivalent to 2 quarters? Can anyone give me a different fraction which is equivalent to 2 quarters? What does 'equivalent' mean?*

### Further activities

- Make a set of cards showing the following fractions:
  $\frac{1}{2}, \frac{2}{4}, \frac{5}{10}, \frac{1}{4}, \frac{2}{8}, \frac{4}{8}, \frac{3}{6}, \frac{1}{5}, \frac{2}{10}, \frac{4}{4}, \frac{2}{2}, \frac{5}{5}, \frac{10}{10}, 1$
  Make some other cards with these fractions shown as a fraction of a shape.

Use the cards for games and activities such as 'Snap', 'Pelmanism', ordering a selection on a line so that equivalent fractions are in the same position and a version of 'Happy Families' with fraction families being made.

## Recognizing equivalent fractions

Look at this equivalent strip.
It can help you to compare fractions.

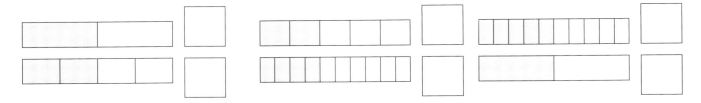

| whole | | | | | | | | | |
| halves | | | | | | | | | |
| quarters | | | | | | | | | |
| fifths | | | | | | | | | |
| tenths | | | | | | | | | |

Write these pairs of equivalent fractions.

Circle the odd one out in each of these boxes.

| | |
|---|---|
| $\frac{5}{10}$ | $\frac{3}{5}$ |
| $\frac{2}{4}$ | $\frac{1}{2}$ |

| | |
|---|---|
| $\frac{3}{5}$ | $\frac{3}{4}$ |
| | $\frac{6}{10}$ |

| | |
|---|---|
| $\frac{4}{10}$ | |
| | $\frac{1}{4}$ |
| $\frac{2}{5}$ | |

| | |
|---|---|
| $\frac{2}{2}$ | $\frac{4}{5}$ |
| $\frac{10}{10}$ | $\frac{4}{4}$ |

Colour these rectangles to show equivalent fractions.

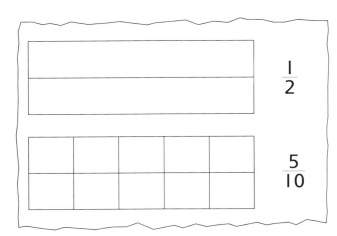

$\frac{1}{2}$

$\frac{5}{10}$

$\frac{6}{10}$

$\frac{3}{5}$

**Key Lessons in Numeracy:**
Numbers and the Number System Year 3

## Recognizing equivalent fractions

Colour half of each of these shapes.

Write the equivalent fraction to $\frac{1}{2}$.

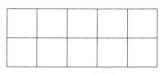

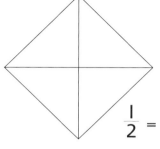

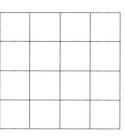

$\frac{1}{2} = \frac{\square}{\square}$

$\frac{1}{2} = \frac{\square}{\square}$

$\frac{1}{2} = \frac{\square}{\square}$

$\frac{1}{2} = \frac{\square}{\square}$

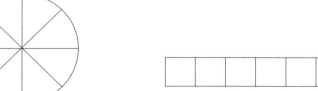

$\frac{1}{2} = \frac{\square}{\square}$

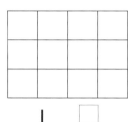

$\frac{1}{2} = \frac{\square}{\square}$

---

## Recognizing equivalent fractions

1. ☐  2. ☐  3. ☐

Write these pairs of equivalent fractions.

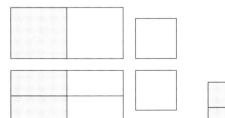

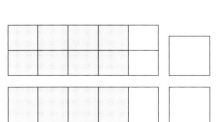

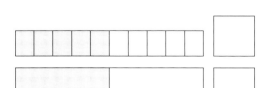

**Key Lessons in Numeracy:**
Numbers and the Number System Year 3

**Comparing fractions**

### Lesson objective

- to compare familiar fractions

### Language

- fraction, one half, one quarter, three quarters, one and a half, two and a quarter, four and three quarters, and so on, mixed number

### Resources

- individual strips of thin card, a number line (which you might draw on the board) marked 0 to 10 and showing whole, half and quarter numbers, counting stick, **PCM20a, 20b, 20c**

### Prior learning

- recognizing equivalence in simple fractions

---

**Teaching**     *whole class: about 20 minutes*

- Explain to the children that this lesson is about comparing the size of fractions and putting them in order of size.

- Provide each child with a strip of thin card. Ask them to fold their paper strips in half, and then in half again.
  *What fraction of the whole strip is 1 of the 4 equal parts? What fraction of the whole strip is 2 of the 4 equal parts?*
  If the response is 'two quarters', ask for a different fraction which is equivalent to two quarters.
  *Which is the bigger fraction, a quarter or a half? What fraction of the whole strip is 3 of the 4 equal parts? Which is the bigger fraction, three quarters or a half?*

- Draw a line on the board to represent the range 0 to 1 with three short vertical lines in the half and quarter positions. Ask the children what the vertical lines represent and, when you are sure that they understand, write $\frac{1}{4}$, $\frac{1}{2}$ and $\frac{3}{4}$ below the relevant marks. Explain to the children that this represents the relative sizes of the three fractions:
  – $\frac{1}{4}$ being the first mark
  – $\frac{2}{4}$, written as $\frac{1}{2}$, being the second
  – and $\frac{3}{4}$ being the third
  because each position is one quarter more than the previous position.

- Hold up two whole strips and one which is folded in half.
  *How many strips do I have?*
  Repeat this with different mixed numbers including quarters.

- Look at the predrawn number line with all the whole, half and quarter numbers to 10 written in position. Explain to the children that there are quarters and halves marked between each whole number.
  Ask a child to point to the number $4\frac{1}{2}$. Repeat for other mixed numbers including quarters and three quarters.

- Point to a number, such as $3\frac{1}{2}$, and ask what the number says. Repeat for other mixed numbers. Make sure the children say the numbers correctly.

- Ask the children to count together from 0 to 10 in halves, using the line to help them. Then count in quarters from 0 to 10.
  *Which is bigger, $2\frac{3}{4}$ or $3\frac{1}{2}$?*
  Repeat this using other pairs.

   **Key Lessons in Numeracy:** Numbers and the Number System Year 3

*about 15 minutes*

### Core (for whole class or average attainers)

Explain to the children that they will be working out numbers in different positions on number lines, and ordering mixed numbers by size. Give them **PCM20a** and make sure they understand the activity.

### Extension (for extension lesson or higher attainers)

Tell the children that they will be comparing pairs of fractions and then estimating the position of fractions on a number line. Give out **PCM20b**, making sure they understand the mathematical symbols being used.

### Support (for reinforcement lesson or lower attainers)

If possible, support this activity by using five bars of chocolate, which each have four equal sections (otherwise, use pictures of bars of chocolate). Break one bar into quarters and use a variety of combinations of whole bars and halves and quarters for the children to name. Give each child a copy of **PCM20c** to continue the activity and record their results.

**Plenary**     *whole class: about 5 minutes*

Using the counting stick, point to different positions for the children to count in tenths. Ask individual children to indicate on the stick other fractions, such as half, third, quarter, two thirds, three quarters, and so on.

*Which is bigger, two thirds or one half?*

*Which is bigger, three quarters or nine tenths?*

### Further activities

- Give each child a fraction card with the fractions $\frac{1}{4}$, $\frac{1}{2}$, $\frac{3}{4}$, 1, $1\frac{1}{4}$, $1\frac{1}{2}$, and so on. Ask the children to place their cards correctly on a number line, or line them up in order.

- As an extension, ask the children to find the right partner to make a whole number such as 3 or 5. Make sure it is feasible to make the numbers suggested.

## Comparing fractions

Write the missing numbers on the number lines.

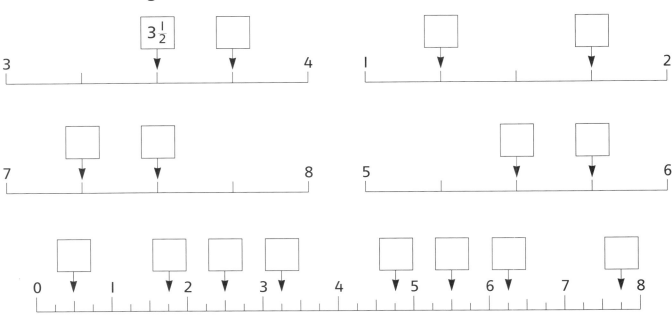

· · · · · · · · · · · · · · · · · · · · · · · · · · · · · · · · · · · · · · · · · · · · · · · · · · · · · · · · ·

Write these distances in order of size, starting with the shortest.

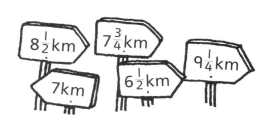

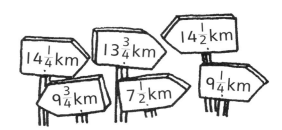

_____ _____ _____     _____ _____ _____

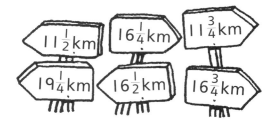

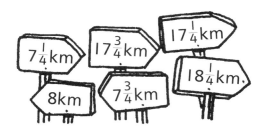

_____ _____ _____     _____ _____ _____

Name: ........................................................................................

## Comparing fractions

Look at these symbols:

| = equals | > is greater than | < is less than |
|---|---|---|

Write = or > or < to make these statements true.

$\frac{1}{2}$ ☐ $\frac{2}{4}$    $\frac{1}{10}$ ☐ $\frac{1}{2}$    $\frac{1}{5}$ ☐ $\frac{1}{4}$    $\frac{3}{5}$ ☐ $\frac{6}{10}$

$3\frac{1}{2}$ ☐ $3\frac{1}{4}$    $4\frac{1}{3}$ ☐ $4\frac{1}{5}$    $6\frac{3}{10}$ ☐ $6\frac{1}{2}$    $7\frac{1}{4}$ ☐ $7\frac{1}{5}$

Now estimate and write these fractions on this number line.

$\frac{1}{2}$    $\frac{1}{4}$    $\frac{3}{4}$    $\frac{1}{3}$    $\frac{1}{5}$    $\frac{9}{10}$    $\frac{2}{3}$

0 |—————————————————————————————| 1

---

Name: ........................................................................................

## Comparing fractions

This is a whole bar of chocolate.
Write the whole number and fraction shown by these.

 ☐

 ☐

 ☐

Draw chocolate bars to show the fraction $2\frac{3}{4}$.

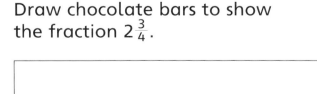

**Key Lessons in Numeracy:**
Numbers and the Number System Year 3

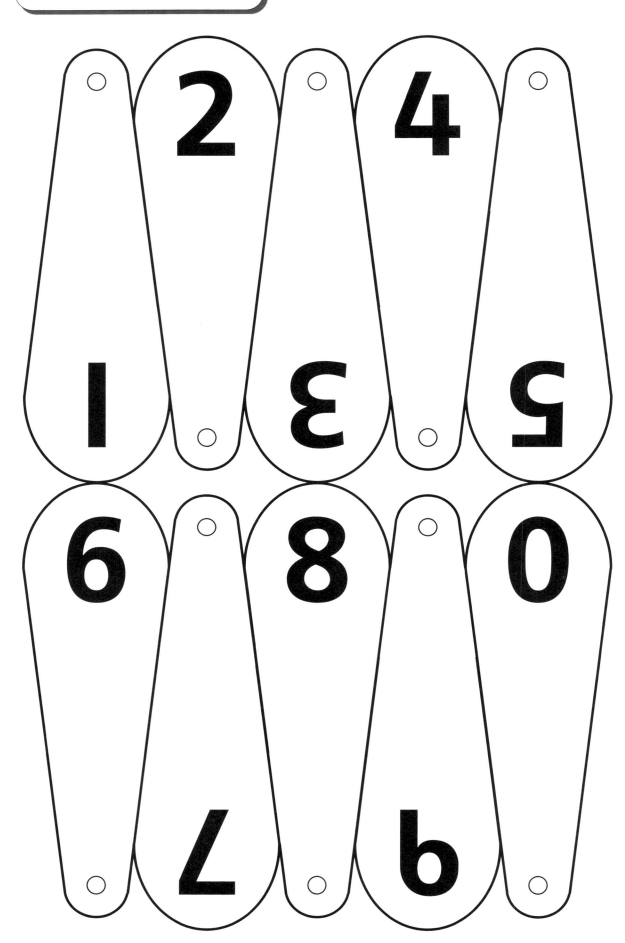

## Resource sheet 2    Digit cards

| | | |
|---|---|---|
| 0 | 1 | 2 |
| 3 | 4 | 5 |
| 6 | 7 | 8 |
| | 9 | |

# Resource sheet 3  1–100 squares

| 1 | 2 | 3 | 4 | 5 | 6 | 7 | 8 | 9 | 10 |
|---|---|---|---|---|---|---|---|---|---|
| 11 | 12 | 13 | 14 | 15 | 16 | 17 | 18 | 19 | 20 |
| 21 | 22 | 23 | 24 | 25 | 26 | 27 | 28 | 29 | 30 |
| 31 | 32 | 33 | 34 | 35 | 36 | 37 | 38 | 39 | 40 |
| 41 | 42 | 43 | 44 | 45 | 46 | 47 | 48 | 49 | 50 |
| 51 | 52 | 53 | 54 | 55 | 56 | 57 | 58 | 59 | 60 |
| 61 | 62 | 63 | 64 | 65 | 66 | 67 | 68 | 69 | 70 |
| 71 | 72 | 73 | 74 | 75 | 76 | 77 | 78 | 79 | 80 |
| 81 | 82 | 83 | 84 | 85 | 86 | 87 | 88 | 89 | 90 |
| 91 | 92 | 93 | 94 | 95 | 96 | 97 | 98 | 99 | 100 |

| 1 | 2 | 3 | 4 | 5 | 6 | 7 | 8 | 9 | 10 |
|---|---|---|---|---|---|---|---|---|---|
| 11 | 12 | 13 | 14 | 15 | 16 | 17 | 18 | 19 | 20 |
| 21 | 22 | 23 | 24 | 25 | 26 | 27 | 28 | 29 | 30 |
| 31 | 32 | 33 | 34 | 35 | 36 | 37 | 38 | 39 | 40 |
| 41 | 42 | 43 | 44 | 45 | 46 | 47 | 48 | 49 | 50 |
| 51 | 52 | 53 | 54 | 55 | 56 | 57 | 58 | 59 | 60 |
| 61 | 62 | 63 | 64 | 65 | 66 | 67 | 68 | 69 | 70 |
| 71 | 72 | 73 | 74 | 75 | 76 | 77 | 78 | 79 | 80 |
| 81 | 82 | 83 | 84 | 85 | 86 | 87 | 88 | 89 | 90 |
| 91 | 92 | 93 | 94 | 95 | 96 | 97 | 98 | 99 | 100 |

**Key Lessons in Numeracy:**
Numbers and the Number System Year 3

| | | |
|---|---|---|
| 1 0 0 0 | 0 0 6 | 1 0 \ 6 |
| 2 0 0 0 | 0 0 8 | 2 0 \ 8 |
| 3 0 0 0 | 0 0 7 | 3 0 \ 7 |
| 4 0 0 0 | 0 0 9 | 4 0 \ 9 |
| 5 0 0 0 | 0 0 5 | 5 0 \ 5 |
| 6 0 0 0 | 0 0 4 | 6 0 \ 4 |
| 7 0 0 0 | 0 0 3 | 7 0 \ 3 |
| 8 0 0 0 | 0 0 2 | 8 0 \ 2 |
| 9 0 0 0 | 0 0 1 | 9 0 \ 1 |

| | | |
|---|---|---|
| £1·00 | 06 | 1 |
| £2·00 | 08 | 2 |
| £3·00 | 07 | 3 |
| £4·00 | 09 | 4 |
| £5·00 | 05 | 5 |
| £6·00 | 04 | 6 |
| £7·00 | 03 | 7 |
| £8·00 | 02 | 8 |
| £9·00 | 01 | 9 |

## Resource sheet 6   Number lines

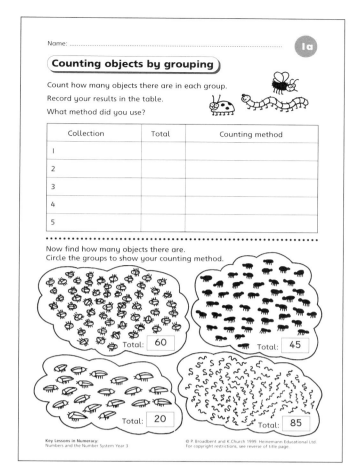

Name: ...........................................................

**1a**

## Counting objects by grouping

Count how many objects there are in each group.
Record your results in the table.
What method did you use?

| Collection | Total | Counting method |
|------------|-------|-----------------|
| 1 | | |
| 2 | | |
| 3 | | |
| 4 | | |
| 5 | | |

Now find how many objects there are.
Circle the groups to show your counting method.

Total: 60

Total: 45

Total: 20

Total: 85

Key Lessons in Numeracy:
Numbers and the Number System Year 3

© P. Broadbent and K.Church 1999  Heinemann Educational Ltd.
For copyright restrictions, see reverse of title page.

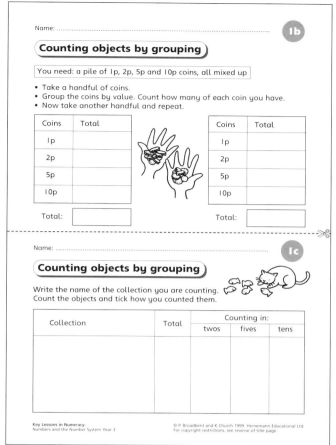

Name: ...........................................................

**1b**

## Counting objects by grouping

You need: a pile of 1p, 2p, 5p and 10p coins, all mixed up

• Take a handful of coins.
• Group the coins by value. Count how many of each coin you have.
• Now take another handful and repeat.

| Coins | Total |
|-------|-------|
| 1p | |
| 2p | |
| 5p | |
| 10p | |

Total: 

| Coins | Total |
|-------|-------|
| 1p | |
| 2p | |
| 5p | |
| 10p | |

Total: 

Name: ...........................................................

**1c**

## Counting objects by grouping

Write the name of the collection you are counting.
Count the objects and tick how you counted them.

| Collection | Total | Counting in: | | |
|------------|-------|------|-------|------|
| | | twos | fives | tens |
| | | | | |
| | | | | |
| | | | | |

Key Lessons in Numeracy:
Numbers and the Number System Year 3

© P. Broadbent and K.Church 1999  Heinemann Educational Ltd
For copyright restrictions, see reverse of title page.

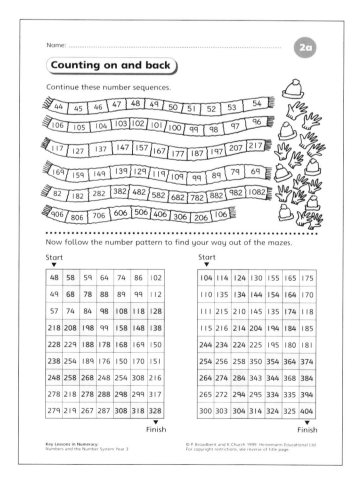

Name: ...........................................................

**2a**

## Counting on and back

Continue these number sequences.

44  45  46  47  48  49  50  51  52  53  54
106  105  104  103  102  101  100  99  98  97  96
117  127  137  147  157  167  177  187  197  207  217
169  159  149  139  129  119  109  99  89  79  69
82  182  282  382  482  582  682  782  882  982  1082
906  806  706  606  506  406  306  206  106

Now follow the number pattern to find your way out of the mazes.

Start ▼

| 48 | 58 | 59 | 64 | 74 | 86 | 102 |
|----|----|----|----|----|----|-----|
| 49 | 68 | 78 | 88 | 89 | 99 | 112 |
| 57 | 74 | 84 | 98 | 108 | 118 | 128 |
| 218 | 208 | 198 | 99 | 158 | 148 | 138 |
| 228 | 229 | 188 | 178 | 168 | 169 | 150 |
| 238 | 254 | 189 | 176 | 150 | 170 | 151 |
| 248 | 258 | 268 | 248 | 254 | 308 | 216 |
| 278 | 218 | 278 | 288 | 298 | 299 | 317 |
| 279 | 219 | 267 | 287 | 308 | 318 | 328 |

Finish

Start ▼

| 104 | 114 | 124 | 130 | 155 | 165 | 175 |
|-----|-----|-----|-----|-----|-----|-----|
| 110 | 135 | 134 | 144 | 154 | 164 | 170 |
| 111 | 215 | 210 | 145 | 135 | 174 | 118 |
| 115 | 216 | 214 | 204 | 194 | 184 | 185 |
| 244 | 234 | 224 | 225 | 195 | 180 | 181 |
| 254 | 256 | 258 | 350 | 354 | 364 | 374 |
| 264 | 274 | 284 | 343 | 344 | 368 | 384 |
| 265 | 272 | 294 | 295 | 334 | 335 | 394 |
| 300 | 303 | 304 | 314 | 324 | 325 | 404 |

Finish

Key Lessons in Numeracy:
Numbers and the Number System Year 3

© P. Broadbent and K.Church 1999  Heinemann Educational Ltd
For copyright restrictions, see reverse of title page.

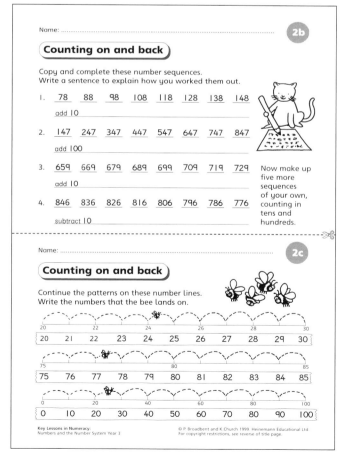

Name: ...........................................................

**2b**

## Counting on and back

Copy and complete these number sequences.
Write a sentence to explain how you worked them out.

1. 78  88  98  108  118  128  138  148
   add 10

2. 147  247  347  447  547  647  747  847
   add 100

3. 659  669  679  689  699  709  719  729
   add 10

4. 846  836  826  816  806  796  786  776
   subtract 10

Now make up five more sequences of your own, counting in tens and hundreds.

Name: ...........................................................

**2c**

## Counting on and back

Continue the patterns on these number lines.
Write the numbers that the bee lands on.

20 ... 22 ... 24 ... 26 ... 28 ... 30
20  21  22  23  24  25  26  27  28  29  30

75 ... 80 ... 85
75  76  77  78  79  80  81  82  83  84  85

0 ... 20 ... 40 ... 60 ... 80 ... 100
0  10  20  30  40  50  60  70  80  90  100

Key Lessons in Numeracy:
Numbers and the Number System Year 3

© P. Broadbent and K.Church 1999  Heinemann Educational Ltd
For copyright restrictions, see reverse of title page.

## 3a

Name: .................................................

### Odd and even numbers

Write the missing numbers in these sequences.
Are the sequences odd or even?

odd or even?

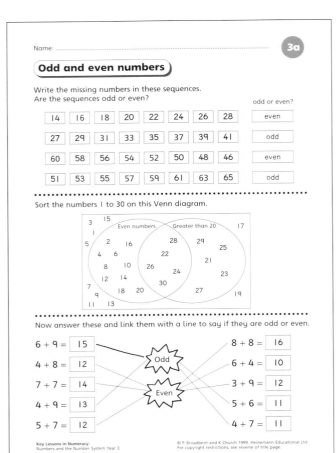

| 14 | 16 | 18 | 20 | 22 | 24 | 26 | 28 | even |
| 27 | 29 | 31 | 33 | 35 | 37 | 39 | 41 | odd |
| 60 | 58 | 56 | 54 | 52 | 50 | 48 | 46 | even |
| 51 | 53 | 55 | 57 | 59 | 61 | 63 | 65 | odd |

Sort the numbers 1 to 30 on this Venn diagram.

Even numbers — Greater than 20

Now answer these and link them with a line to say if they are odd or even.

6 + 9 = 15
4 + 8 = 12
7 + 7 = 14
4 + 9 = 13
5 + 7 = 12

Odd
Even

8 + 8 = 16
6 + 4 = 10
3 + 9 = 12
5 + 6 = 11
4 + 7 = 11

Key Lessons in Numeracy:
Numbers and the Number System Year 3

© P. Broadbent and K.Church 1999  Heinemann Educational Ltd.
For copyright restrictions, see reverse of title page.

## 3b

Name: .................................................

### Odd and even numbers

Complete this addition square.

Look for any patterns you can see.

Use the square to help you to complete these:

even or odd?

even + even = even

even + odd = odd

odd + odd = even

odd + even = odd

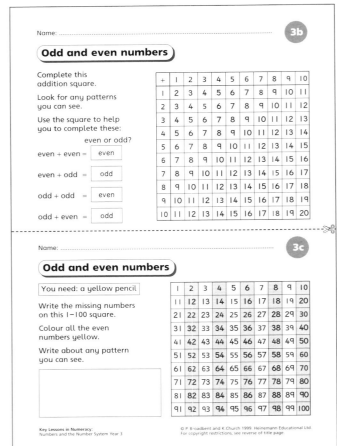

| + | 1 | 2 | 3 | 4 | 5 | 6 | 7 | 8 | 9 | 10 |
|---|---|---|---|---|---|---|---|---|---|----|
| 1 | 2 | 3 | 4 | 5 | 6 | 7 | 8 | 9 | 10 | 11 |
| 2 | 3 | 4 | 5 | 6 | 7 | 8 | 9 | 10 | 11 | 12 |
| 3 | 4 | 5 | 6 | 7 | 8 | 9 | 10 | 11 | 12 | 13 |
| 4 | 5 | 6 | 7 | 8 | 9 | 10 | 11 | 12 | 13 | 14 |
| 5 | 6 | 7 | 8 | 9 | 10 | 11 | 12 | 13 | 14 | 15 |
| 6 | 7 | 8 | 9 | 10 | 11 | 12 | 13 | 14 | 15 | 16 |
| 7 | 8 | 9 | 10 | 11 | 12 | 13 | 14 | 15 | 16 | 17 |
| 8 | 9 | 10 | 11 | 12 | 13 | 14 | 15 | 16 | 17 | 18 |
| 9 | 10 | 11 | 12 | 13 | 14 | 15 | 16 | 17 | 18 | 19 |
| 10 | 11 | 12 | 13 | 14 | 15 | 16 | 17 | 18 | 19 | 20 |

## 3c

Name: .................................................

### Odd and even numbers

You need: a yellow pencil

Write the missing numbers on this 1–100 square.

Colour all the even numbers yellow.

Write about any pattern you can see.

| 1 | 2 | 3 | 4 | 5 | 6 | 7 | 8 | 9 | 10 |
|---|---|---|---|---|---|---|---|---|----|
| 11 | 12 | 13 | 14 | 15 | 16 | 17 | 18 | 19 | 20 |
| 21 | 22 | 23 | 24 | 25 | 26 | 27 | 28 | 29 | 30 |
| 31 | 32 | 33 | 34 | 35 | 36 | 37 | 38 | 39 | 40 |
| 41 | 42 | 43 | 44 | 45 | 46 | 47 | 48 | 49 | 50 |
| 51 | 52 | 53 | 54 | 55 | 56 | 57 | 58 | 59 | 60 |
| 61 | 62 | 63 | 64 | 65 | 66 | 67 | 68 | 69 | 70 |
| 71 | 72 | 73 | 74 | 75 | 76 | 77 | 78 | 79 | 80 |
| 81 | 82 | 83 | 84 | 85 | 86 | 87 | 88 | 89 | 90 |
| 91 | 92 | 93 | 94 | 95 | 96 | 97 | 98 | 99 | 100 |

Key Lessons in Numeracy:
Numbers and the Number System Year 3

© P. Broadbent and K.Church 1999  Heinemann Educational Ltd.
For copyright restrictions, see reverse of title page.

## 4a

Name: .................................................

### Counting patterns

Continue these number sequences.

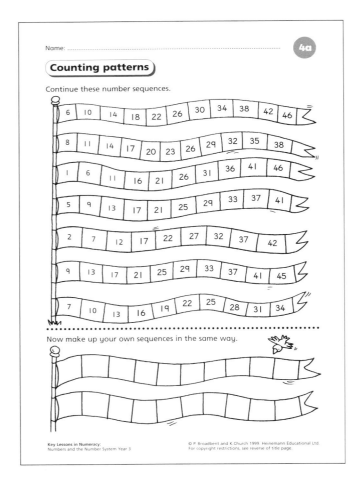

6 10 14 18 22 26 30 34 38 42 46

8 11 14 17 20 23 26 29 32 35 38

1 6 11 16 21 26 31 36 41 46

5 9 13 17 21 25 29 33 37 41

2 7 12 17 22 27 32 37 42

9 13 17 21 25 29 33 37 41 45

7 10 13 16 19 22 25 28 31 34

Now make up your own sequences in the same way.

Key Lessons in Numeracy:
Numbers and the Number System Year 3

© P. Broadbent and K.Church 1999  Heinemann Educational Ltd.
For copyright restrictions, see reverse of title page.

## 4b

Name: .................................................

### Counting patterns

Copy and complete these number sequences.
Write a sentence with each one to explain how you worked it out.

1  3 8 13 18 23 28 33 38 43 48    add 5

2  7 11 15 19 23 27 31 35 39 43    add 4

3  5 8 11 14 17 20 23 26 29 32    add 3

4  46 41 36 31 26 21 16 11 6 1    subtract 5

5  50 46 42 38 34 30 26 22 18 14    subtract 4

Now make up five more sequences of your own using different steps.

## 4c

Name: .................................................

### Counting patterns

Complete these number sequences by counting on in fives.

| 3 | 8 | 13 | 18 | 23 | 28 | 33 | 38 | 43 | 48 |

| 6 | 11 | 16 | 21 | 26 | 31 | 36 | 41 | 46 | 51 |

Choose a number and count on in fives. ▶

Complete these number sequences by counting on in threes.

| 8 | 11 | 14 | 17 | 20 | 23 | 26 | 29 | 32 | 35 |

| 10 | 13 | 16 | 19 | 22 | 25 | 28 | 31 | 34 | 37 |

Choose a number and count on in threes. ▶

Key Lessons in Numeracy:
Numbers and the Number System Year 3

© P. Broadbent and K.Church 1999  Heinemann Educational Ltd.
For copyright restrictions, see reverse of title page.

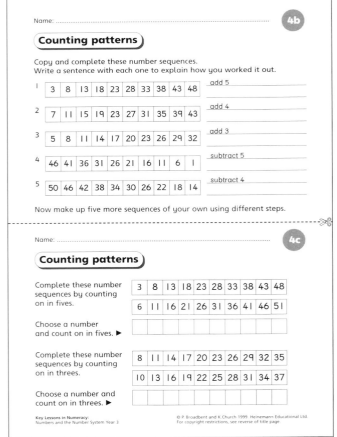

Name: ...............................................................

## Recognizing 2-digit multiples

Write these sets of numbers in each Venn diagram.

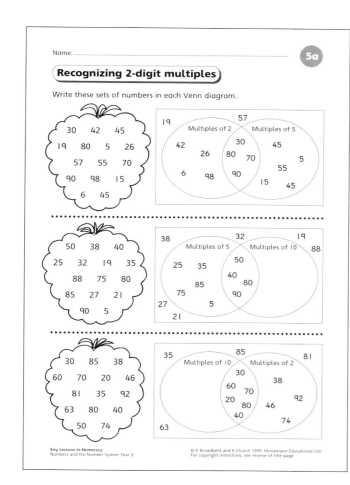

Name: ...............................................................

## Recognizing 2-digit multiples

Write the numbers 1 to 100 in this Venn diagram.

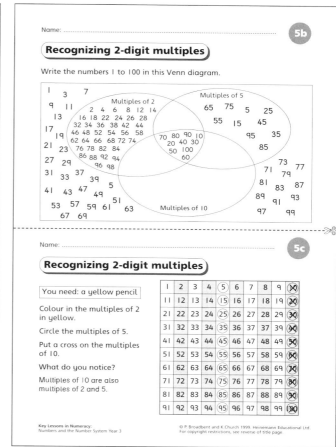

## Recognizing 2-digit multiples

You need: a yellow pencil

Colour in the multiples of 2 in yellow.

Circle the multiples of 5.

Put a cross on the multiples of 10.

What do you notice?

Multiples of 10 are also multiples of 2 and 5.

| 1 | 2 | 3 | 4 | (5) | 6 | 7 | 8 | 9 | (X) |
|---|---|---|---|---|---|---|---|---|---|
| 11 | 12 | 13 | 14 | (15) | 16 | 17 | 18 | 19 | (X) |
| 21 | 22 | 23 | 24 | (25) | 26 | 27 | 28 | 29 | (X) |
| 31 | 32 | 33 | 34 | (35) | 36 | 37 | 37 | 39 | (X) |
| 41 | 42 | 43 | 44 | (45) | 46 | 47 | 48 | 49 | (X) |
| 51 | 52 | 53 | 54 | (55) | 56 | 57 | 58 | 59 | (X) |
| 61 | 62 | 63 | 64 | (65) | 66 | 67 | 68 | 69 | (X) |
| 71 | 72 | 73 | 74 | (75) | 76 | 77 | 78 | 79 | (X) |
| 81 | 82 | 83 | 84 | (85) | 86 | 87 | 88 | 89 | (X) |
| 91 | 92 | 93 | 94 | (95) | 96 | 97 | 98 | 99 | (X) |

Name: ...............................................................

## Recognizing 3-digit multiples

Write these sets of numbers in each Carroll diagram.

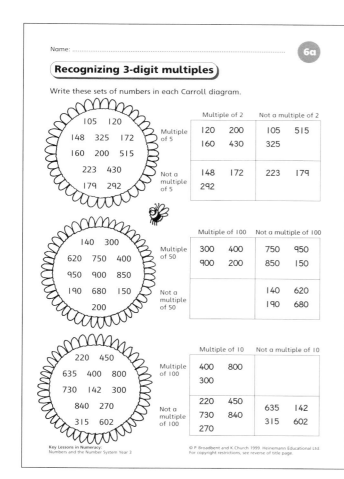

Name: ...............................................................

## Recognizing 3-digit multiples

Write these numbers in this Carroll diagram.

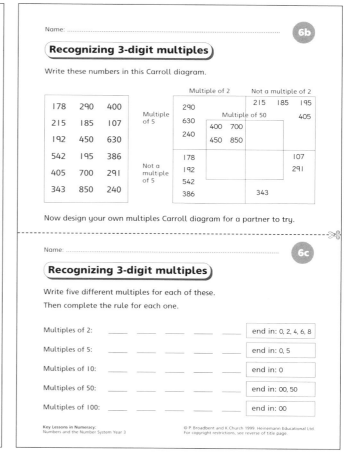

Now design your own multiples Carroll diagram for a partner to try.

Name: ...............................................................

## Recognizing 3-digit multiples

Write five different multiples for each of these.
Then complete the rule for each one.

| | | | | | | |
|---|---|---|---|---|---|---|
| Multiples of 2: | ___ | ___ | ___ | ___ | ___ | end in: 0, 2, 4, 6, 8 |
| Multiples of 5: | ___ | ___ | ___ | ___ | ___ | end in: 0, 5 |
| Multiples of 10: | ___ | ___ | ___ | ___ | ___ | end in: 0 |
| Multiples of 50: | ___ | ___ | ___ | ___ | ___ | end in: 00, 50 |
| Multiples of 100: | ___ | ___ | ___ | ___ | ___ | end in: 00 |

Name: .................................................. **7a**

## Reading and writing numbers to 1000

Write the answers to this cross-number.

*Across*
1  seven hundred and twenty-five
3  two hundred and ninety-four
5  one hundred and sixty-seven
6  one hundred and twenty-four
8  one hundred and twenty-six
10 two hundred and ninety-three
12 seven hundred and eight
14 three hundred and forty
15 five hundred and three
16 two hundred and ninety

*Down*
1  seven hundred and forty-one
2  five hundred and fourteen
3  two hundred and seventy-one
4  four hundred and six
7  two hundred and nineteen
9  two hundred and ninety
10 two hundred and five
11 three hundred and thirty-three
12 seven hundred and two
13 eight hundred and twenty

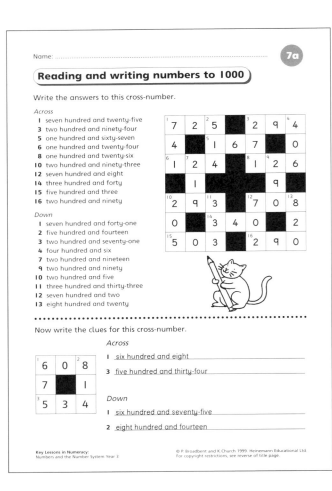

Now write the clues for this cross-number.

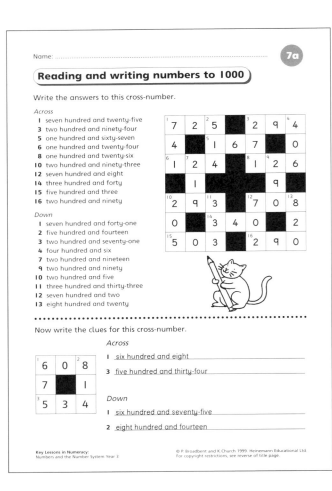

*Across*
1  six hundred and eight _____
3  five hundred and thirty-four _____

*Down*
1  six hundred and seventy-five _____
2  eight hundred and fourteen _____

Key Lessons in Numeracy:
Numbers and the Number System Year 3
© P. Broadbent and K.Church 1999. Heinemann Educational Ltd.
For copyright restrictions, see reverse of title page.

---

Name: .................................................. **7b**

## Reading and writing numbers to 1000

Read the clues below and write the numbers as numerals and as words.

I have 6 hundreds, 8 tens and a single unit. What number am I?
**681**   six hundred and eighty-one

I have no units, 5 tens and 2 hundreds. What number am I?
**250**   two hundred and fifty

My hundreds and tens digits are the same and total 10. My units digit is the next even digit after 6. What number am I?
**558**   five hundred and fifty-eight

I have no tens digit and the other two digits total 9. I am a number between 100 and 120. What number am I?
**108**   one hundred and eight

Now make up your own clues for numbers.

---

Name: .................................................. **7c**

## Reading and writing numbers to 1000

Complete these, following your teacher's instructions.

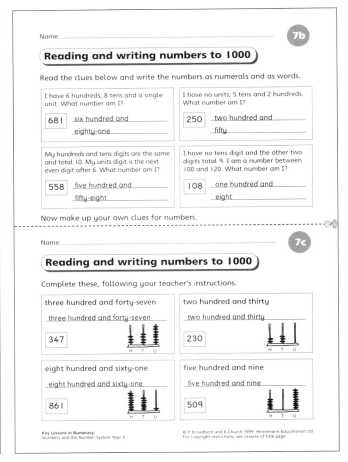

three hundred and forty-seven
three hundred and forty-seven
**347**

two hundred and thirty
two hundred and thirty
**230**

eight hundred and sixty-one
eight hundred and sixty-one
**861**

five hundred and nine
five hundred and nine
**509**

Key Lessons in Numeracy:
Numbers and the Number System Year 3
© P. Broadbent and K.Church 1999. Heinemann Educational Ltd.
For copyright restrictions, see reverse of title page.

---

Name: .................................................. **8a**

## Recognizing hundreds, tens and units

You need: some counters

Place the counters on this abacus to show the different numbers.

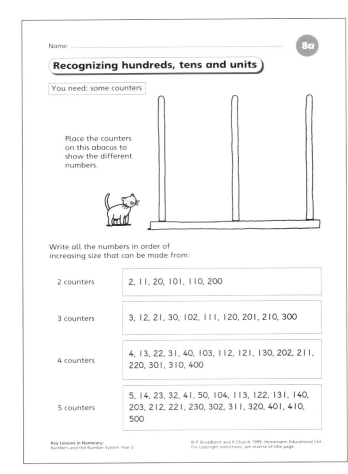

Write all the numbers in order of increasing size that can be made from:

2 counters  |  2, 11, 20, 101, 110, 200

3 counters  |  3, 12, 21, 30, 102, 111, 120, 201, 210, 300

4 counters  |  4, 13, 22, 31, 40, 103, 112, 121, 130, 202, 211, 220, 301, 310, 400

5 counters  |  5, 14, 23, 32, 41, 50, 104, 113, 122, 131, 140, 203, 212, 221, 230, 302, 311, 320, 401, 410, 500

Key Lessons in Numeracy:
Numbers and the Number System Year 3
© P. Broadbent and K.Church 1999. Heinemann Educational Ltd.
For copyright restrictions, see reverse of title page.

---

Name: .................................................. **8b**

## Recognizing hundreds, tens and units

You will need: decahedral dice

**Game 1**
Highest number
Throw the dice three times.
a ☐☐☐   b ☐☐☐   c ☐☐☐   d ☐☐☐

**Game 2**
Highest total
Throw the dice nine times.
☐☐☐ + ☐☐☐ + ☐☐☐ = ☐☐☐

**Game 3**
Lowest number
Throw the dice three times.
a ☐☐☐   b ☐☐☐   c ☐☐☐   d ☐☐☐

---

Name: .................................................. **8c**

## Recognizing hundreds, tens and units

Write these sets of numbers in order of size, starting with the smallest.

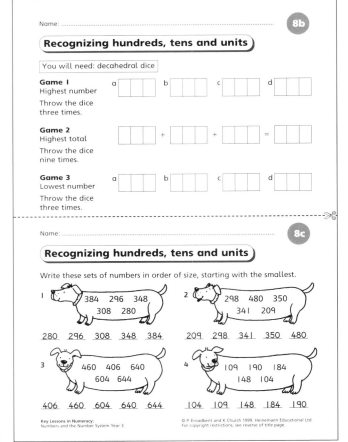

1  384  296  348  308  280
280  296  308  348  384

2  298  480  350  341  209
209  298  341  350  480

3  460  406  640  604  644
406  460  604  640  644

4  109  190  184  148  104
104  109  148  184  190

Key Lessons in Numeracy:
Numbers and the Number System Year 3
© P. Broadbent and K.Church 1999. Heinemann Educational Ltd.
For copyright restrictions, see reverse of title page.

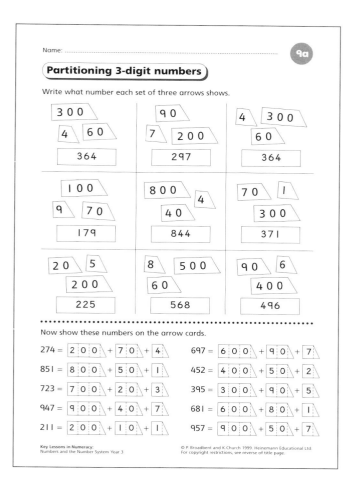

Name: .................................................

**9a**

### Partitioning 3-digit numbers

Write what number each set of three arrows shows.

| 300 / 4 / 60 → 364 | 90 / 7 / 200 → 297 | 4 / 300 / 60 → 364 |
| 100 / 9 / 70 → 179 | 800 / 4 / 40 → 844 | 70 / 1 / 300 → 371 |
| 20 / 5 / 200 → 225 | 8 / 500 / 60 → 568 | 90 / 6 / 400 → 496 |

Now show these numbers on the arrow cards.

274 = 200 + 70 + 4        697 = 600 + 90 + 7
851 = 800 + 50 + 1        452 = 400 + 50 + 2
723 = 700 + 20 + 3        395 = 300 + 90 + 5
947 = 900 + 40 + 7        681 = 600 + 80 + 1
211 = 200 + 10 + 1        957 = 900 + 50 + 7

Key Lessons in Numeracy:
Numbers and the Number System Year 3

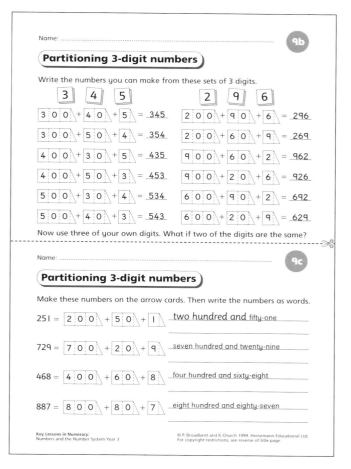

Name: .................................................

**9b**

### Partitioning 3-digit numbers

Write the numbers you can make from these sets of 3 digits.

| 3 | 4 | 5 | | 2 | 9 | 6 |

300 + 40 + 5 = 345        200 + 90 + 6 = 296
300 + 50 + 4 = 354        200 + 60 + 9 = 269
400 + 30 + 5 = 435        900 + 60 + 2 = 962
400 + 50 + 3 = 453        900 + 20 + 6 = 926
500 + 30 + 4 = 534        600 + 90 + 2 = 692
500 + 40 + 3 = 543        600 + 20 + 9 = 629

Now use three of your own digits. What if two of the digits are the same?

- - - - - - - - - - - - - - - - - - - - - - - - - - - - - - - - - - - - - - - - - ✂

Name: .................................................

**9c**

### Partitioning 3-digit numbers

Make these numbers on the arrow cards. Then write the numbers as words.

251 = 200 + 50 + 1   _two hundred and fifty-one_

729 = 700 + 20 + 9   _seven hundred and twenty-nine_

468 = 400 + 60 + 8   _four hundred and sixty-eight_

887 = 800 + 80 + 7   _eight hundred and eighty-seven_

Key Lessons in Numeracy:
Numbers and the Number System Year 3

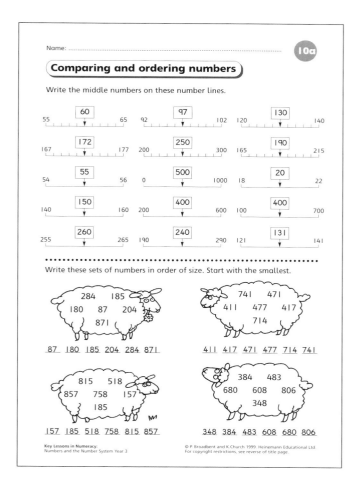

Name: .................................................

**10a**

### Comparing and ordering numbers

Write the middle numbers on these number lines.

55 — 60 — 65        92 — 97 — 102        120 — 130 — 140
167 — 172 — 177      200 — 250 — 300      165 — 190 — 215
54 — 55 — 56        0 — 500 — 1000       18 — 20 — 22
140 — 150 — 160      200 — 400 — 600      100 — 400 — 700
255 — 260 — 265      190 — 240 — 290      121 — 131 — 141

Write these sets of numbers in order of size. Start with the smallest.

284  185  180  87  204  871
_87  180  185  204  284  871_

741  471  411  477  417  714
_411  417  471  477  714  741_

815  518  857  758  157  185
_157  185  518  758  815  857_

384  483  680  608  806  348
_348  384  483  608  680  806_

Key Lessons in Numeracy:
Numbers and the Number System Year 3

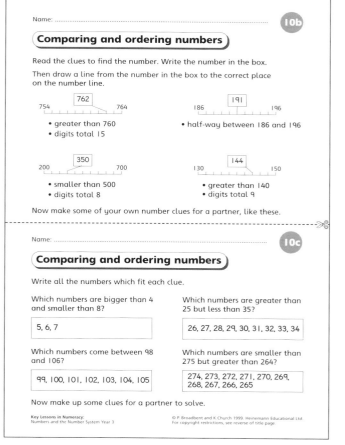

Name: .................................................

**10b**

### Comparing and ordering numbers

Read the clues to find the number. Write the number in the box.
Then draw a line from the number in the box to the correct place
on the number line.

762 — 754 ... 764
- greater than 760
- digits total 15

191 — 186 ... 196
- half-way between 186 and 196

350 — 200 ... 700
- smaller than 500
- digits total 8

144 — 130 ... 150
- greater than 140
- digits total 9

Now make some of your own number clues for a partner, like these.

- - - - - - - - - - - - - - - - - - - - - - - - - - - - - - - - - - - - - - - - - ✂

Name: .................................................

**10c**

### Comparing and ordering numbers

Write all the numbers which fit each clue.

Which numbers are bigger than 4 and smaller than 8?

5, 6, 7

Which numbers are greater than 25 but less than 35?

26, 27, 28, 29, 30, 31, 32, 33, 34

Which numbers come between 98 and 106?

99, 100, 101, 102, 103, 104, 105

Which numbers are smaller than 275 but greater than 264?

274, 273, 272, 271, 270, 269, 268, 267, 266, 265

Now make up some clues for a partner to solve.

Key Lessons in Numeracy:
Numbers and the Number System Year 3

Name: ................................

**11a**

## Changing numbers by 1, 10 and 100

Write the answers.

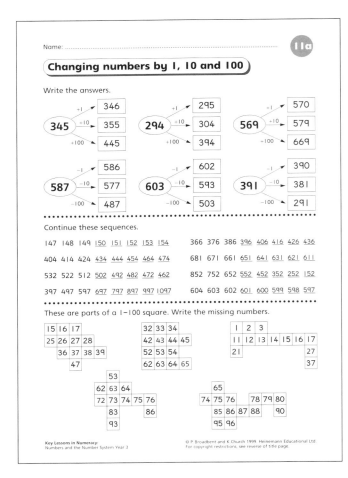

345 → +1 → 346, +10 → 355, +100 → 445

294 → +1 → 295, +10 → 304, +100 → 394

569 → +1 → 570, +10 → 579, +100 → 669

587 → −1 → 586, −10 → 577, −100 → 487

603 → −1 → 602, −10 → 593, −100 → 503

391 → −1 → 390, −10 → 381, −100 → 291

Continue these sequences.

147 148 149 150 151 152 153 154

404 414 424 434 444 454 464 474

532 522 512 502 492 482 472 462

397 497 597 697 797 897 997 1097

366 376 386 396 406 416 426 436

681 671 661 651 641 631 621 611

852 752 652 552 452 352 252 152

604 603 602 601 600 599 598 597

These are parts of a 1–100 square. Write the missing numbers.

15 16 17
25 26 27 28
36 37 38 39
47

32 33 34
42 43 44 45
52 53 54
62 63 64 65

1 2 3
11 12 13 14 15 16 17
21 ... 27
... 37

53
62 63 64
72 73 74 75 76
83 ... 86
93

65
74 75 76 ... 78 79 80
85 86 87 88 ... 90
95 96

---

Name: ................................

**11b**

## Changing numbers by 1, 10 and 100

A game for two players.

You need: arrow cards (hundreds, tens and units)

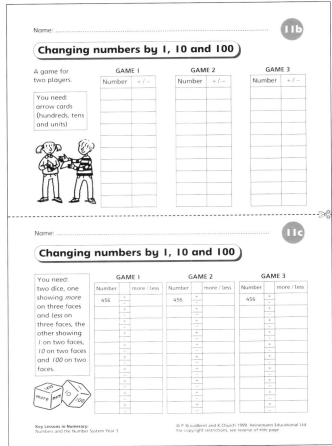

| GAME 1 | | GAME 2 | | GAME 3 | |
|---|---|---|---|---|---|
| Number | + / − | Number | + / − | Number | + / − |
| | | | | | |
| | | | | | |
| | | | | | |
| | | | | | |
| | | | | | |

- - - - - - - - ✂

Name: ................................

**11c**

## Changing numbers by 1, 10 and 100

You need: two dice, one showing *more* on three faces and *less* on three faces, the other showing *1* on two faces, *10* on two faces and *100* on two faces.

| GAME 1 | | GAME 2 | | GAME 3 | |
|---|---|---|---|---|---|
| Number | more / less | Number | more / less | Number | more / less |
| 456 | + | 456 | + | 456 | + |
| | − | | − | | − |
| | + | | + | | + |
| | − | | − | | − |
| | + | | + | | + |
| | − | | − | | − |
| | + | | + | | + |
| | − | | − | | − |
| | + | | + | | + |
| | − | | − | | − |
| | + | | + | | + |
| | − | | − | | − |

---

Name: ................................

**12a**

## Ordering 3-digit numbers

Look at these parts of a number line.
Fill in the missing numbers.

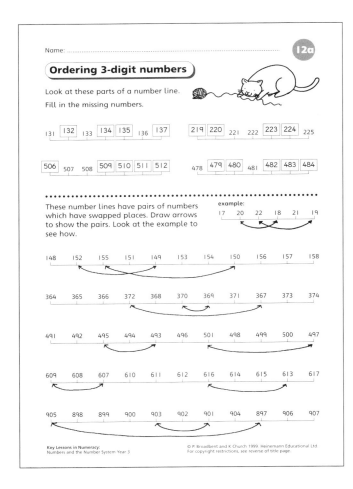

131 132 133 134 135 136 137

219 220 221 222 223 224 225

506 507 508 509 510 511 512

478 479 480 481 482 483 484

These number lines have pairs of numbers which have swapped places. Draw arrows to show the pairs. Look at the example to see how.

example:
17 20 22 18 21 19

148 152 155 151 149 153 154 150 156 157 158

364 365 366 372 368 370 369 371 367 373 374

491 492 495 494 493 496 501 498 499 500 497

609 608 607 610 611 612 616 614 615 613 617

905 898 899 900 903 902 901 904 897 906 907

---

Name: ................................

**12b**

## Ordering 3-digit numbers

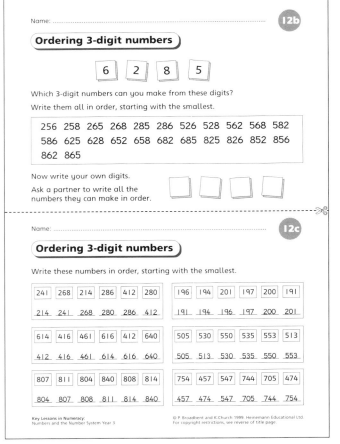

6 2 8 5

Which 3-digit numbers can you make from these digits?
Write them all in order, starting with the smallest.

256 258 265 268 285 286 526 528 562 568 582
586 625 628 652 658 682 685 825 826 852 856
862 865

Now write your own digits.
Ask a partner to write all the numbers they can make in order.

- - - - - - - - ✂

Name: ................................

**12c**

## Ordering 3-digit numbers

Write these numbers in order, starting with the smallest.

| 241 | 268 | 214 | 286 | 412 | 280 |
|---|---|---|---|---|---|
| 214 | 241 | 268 | 280 | 286 | 412 |

| 196 | 194 | 201 | 197 | 200 | 191 |
|---|---|---|---|---|---|
| 191 | 194 | 196 | 197 | 200 | 201 |

| 614 | 416 | 461 | 616 | 412 | 640 |
|---|---|---|---|---|---|
| 412 | 416 | 461 | 614 | 616 | 640 |

| 505 | 530 | 550 | 535 | 553 | 513 |
|---|---|---|---|---|---|
| 505 | 513 | 530 | 535 | 550 | 553 |

| 807 | 811 | 804 | 840 | 808 | 814 |
|---|---|---|---|---|---|
| 804 | 807 | 808 | 811 | 814 | 840 |

| 754 | 457 | 547 | 744 | 705 | 474 |
|---|---|---|---|---|---|
| 457 | 474 | 547 | 705 | 744 | 754 |

## 13a

Name: ..................................................

### Comparing and ordering money

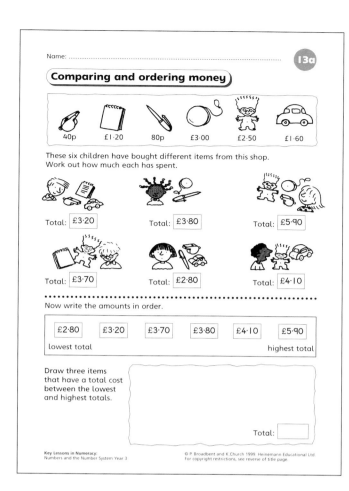

| 40p | £1·20 | 80p | £3·00 | £2·50 | £1·60 |

These six children have bought different items from this shop.
Work out how much each has spent.

Total: £3·20    Total: £3·80    Total: £5·90

Total: £3·70    Total: £2·80    Total: £4·10

Now write the amounts in order.

| £2·80 | £3·20 | £3·70 | £3·80 | £4·10 | £5·90 |

lowest total                                    highest total

Draw three items
that have a total cost
between the lowest
and highest totals.

Total: [　]

## 13b

Name: ..................................................

### Comparing and ordering money

Look at and compare these price lists from 4 different shops.

| Shop A | | | Shop B | | | Shop C | | | Shop D | |
|---|---|---|---|---|---|---|---|---|---|---|
| rubber bone | 90p | | dog collar | £1·60 | | brush | £1·90 | | dog collar | £1·90 |
| dog collar | £2·10 | | rubber bone | £1·20 | | food bowl | £1·40 | | food bowl | £2·60 |
| brush | £1·60 | | food bowl | £1·30 | | dog collar | £1·90 | | brush | £2·10 |
| food bowl | £1·70 | | brush | £2·40 | | rubber bone | £1·10 | | rubber bone | 80p |
| Total: | £6·30 | | Total: | £6·50 | | Total: | £6·30 | | Total: | £7·40 |

|  | lowest cost | | | highest cost |
|---|---|---|---|---|
| rubber bone | 80p | 90p | £1·10 | £1·20 |
| dog collar | £1·60 | £1·90 | £1·90 | £2·10 |
| brush | £1·60 | £1·90 | £2·10 | £2·40 |
| food bowl | £1·30 | £1·40 | £1·70 | £2·60 |

|  | Total |
|---|---|
| lowest cost | £5·30 |
| highest cost | £8·30 |

## 13c

Name: ..................................................

### Comparing and ordering money

Write these prices in order of size, starting with the smallest.

£2·10  £1·80  £1·50  £2·20  80p

80p  £1·50  £1·80  £2·10  £2·20

£3·70  £2·50  £2·60  £3·50  £3·00

£2·50  £2·60  £3·00  £3·50  £3·70

90p  £1·70  £1·80  £1·00  £1·10

90p  £1·00  £1·10  £1·70  £1·80

£4·20  £4·00  £3·80  £3·90  £3·60

£3·60  £3·80  £3·90  £4·00  £4·20

## 14a

Name: ..................................................

### Estimating objects

Estimate the numbers these arrows point to.

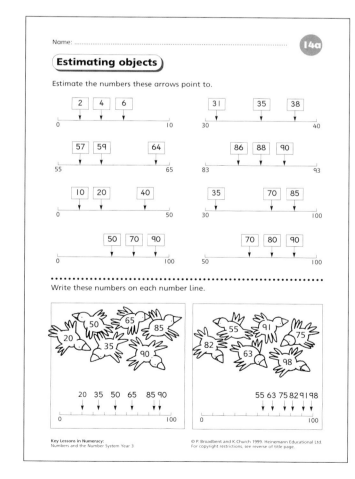

| 2 | 4 | 6 |          | 31 | 35 | 38 |
0                    10    30                40

| 57 | 59 | 64 |        | 86 | 88 | 90 |
55                   65    83                93

| 10 | 20 | 40 |        | 35 | 70 | 85 |
0                    50    30               100

| 50 | 70 | 90 |        | 70 | 80 | 90 |
0                   100    50               100

Write these numbers on each number line.

20  35  50  65  85 90          55 63 75 82 91 98
0                 100    0                  100

## 14b

Name: ..................................................

### Estimating objects

Could you give an accurate estimate for any of these?

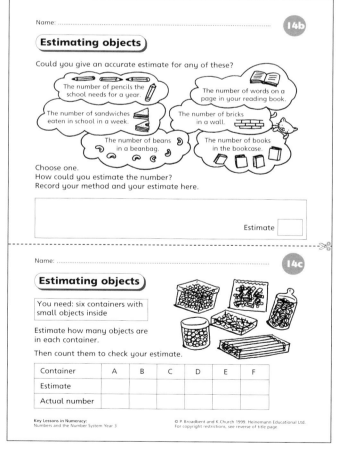

The number of pencils the school needs for a year.

The number of words on a page in your reading book.

The number of sandwiches eaten in school in a week.

The number of bricks in a wall.

The number of beans in a beanbag.

The number of books in the bookcase.

Choose one.
How could you estimate the number?
Record your method and your estimate here.

Estimate [　]

## 14c

Name: ..................................................

### Estimating objects

You need: six containers with small objects inside

Estimate how many objects are in each container.

Then count them to check your estimate.

| Container | A | B | C | D | E | F |
|---|---|---|---|---|---|---|
| Estimate | | | | | | |
| Actual number | | | | | | |

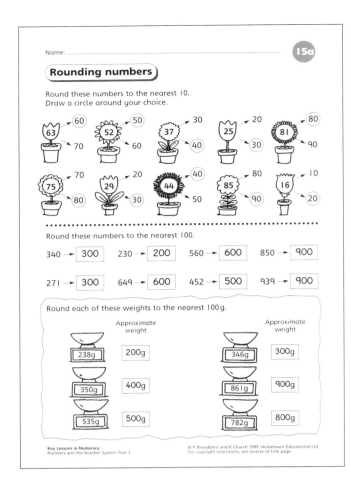

**Rounding numbers** 15a

Round these numbers to the nearest 10.
Draw a circle around your choice.

63 → 60 / 70
52 → 50 / 60
37 → 30 / (40)
25 → 20 / (30)
81 → 80 / 90

75 → 70 / (80)
29 → 20 / (30)
44 → (40) / 50
85 → 80 / (90)
16 → 10 / (20)

Round these numbers to the nearest 100.

340 → 300   230 → 200   560 → 600   850 → 900

271 → 300   649 → 600   452 → 500   939 → 900

Round each of these weights to the nearest 100g.

| | Approximate weight | | | Approximate weight |
|---|---|---|---|---|
| 238g | 200g | | 346g | 300g |
| 350g | 400g | | 861g | 900g |
| 535g | 500g | | 782g | 800g |

Key Lessons in Numeracy:
Numbers and the Number System Year 3

© P. Broadbent and K. Church 1999. Heinemann Educational Ltd.
For copyright restrictions, see reverse of title page.

---

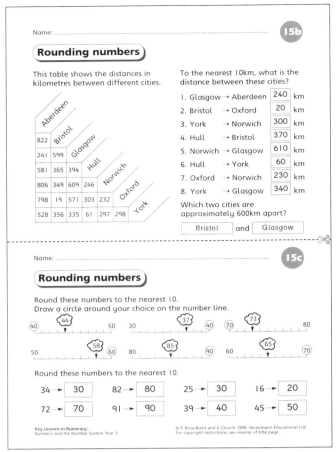

**Rounding numbers** 15b

This table shows the distances in kilometres between different cities.

To the nearest 10km, what is the distance between these cities?

1. Glasgow → Aberdeen    240 km
2. Bristol → Oxford    20 km
3. York → Norwich    300 km
4. Hull → Bristol    370 km
5. Norwich → Glasgow    610 km
6. Hull → York    60 km
7. Oxford → Norwich    230 km
8. York → Glasgow    340 km

Which two cities are approximately 600km apart?

Bristol  and  Glasgow

**Rounding numbers** 15c

Round these numbers to the nearest 10.
Draw a circle around your choice on the number line.

Round these numbers to the nearest 10.

34 → 30    82 → 80    25 → 30    16 → 20
72 → 70    91 → 90    39 → 40    45 → 50

Key Lessons in Numeracy:
Numbers and the Number System Year 3

© P. Broadbent and K. Church 1999. Heinemann Educational Ltd.
For copyright restrictions, see reverse of title page.

---

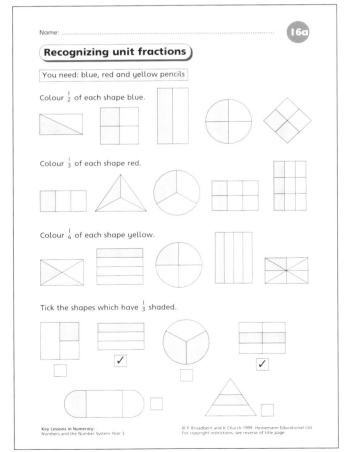

**Recognizing unit fractions** 16a

You need: blue, red and yellow pencils

Colour $\frac{1}{2}$ of each shape blue.

Colour $\frac{1}{3}$ of each shape red.

Colour $\frac{1}{4}$ of each shape yellow.

Tick the shapes which have $\frac{1}{3}$ shaded.

Key Lessons in Numeracy:
Numbers and the Number System Year 3

© P. Broadbent and K. Church 1999. Heinemann Educational Ltd.
For copyright restrictions, see reverse of title page.

---

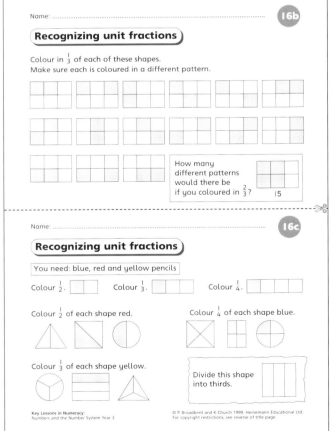

**Recognizing unit fractions** 16b

Colour in $\frac{1}{3}$ of each of these shapes.
Make sure each is coloured in a different pattern.

How many different patterns would there be if you coloured in $\frac{2}{3}$?    15

**Recognizing unit fractions** 16c

You need: blue, red and yellow pencils

Colour $\frac{1}{2}$.    Colour $\frac{1}{3}$.    Colour $\frac{1}{4}$.

Colour $\frac{1}{2}$ of each shape red.    Colour $\frac{1}{4}$ of each shape blue.

Colour $\frac{1}{3}$ of each shape yellow.

Divide this shape into thirds.

Key Lessons in Numeracy:
Numbers and the Number System Year 3

© P. Broadbent and K. Church 1999. Heinemann Educational Ltd.
For copyright restrictions, see reverse of title page.

---

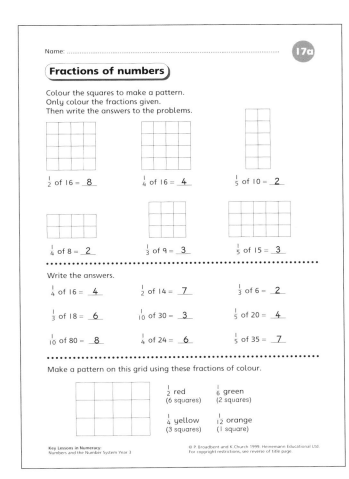

Name: .................................................

17a

**Fractions of numbers**

Colour the squares to make a pattern.
Only colour the fractions given.
Then write the answers to the problems.

$\frac{1}{2}$ of 16 = _8_    $\frac{1}{4}$ of 16 = _4_    $\frac{1}{5}$ of 10 = _2_

$\frac{1}{4}$ of 8 = _2_    $\frac{1}{3}$ of 9 = _3_    $\frac{1}{5}$ of 15 = _3_

Write the answers.

$\frac{1}{4}$ of 16 = _4_    $\frac{1}{2}$ of 14 = _7_    $\frac{1}{3}$ of 6 = _2_

$\frac{1}{3}$ of 18 = _6_    $\frac{1}{10}$ of 30 = _3_    $\frac{1}{5}$ of 20 = _4_

$\frac{1}{10}$ of 80 = _8_    $\frac{1}{4}$ of 24 = _6_    $\frac{1}{5}$ of 35 = _7_

Make a pattern on this grid using these fractions of colour.

$\frac{1}{2}$ red (6 squares)    $\frac{1}{6}$ green (2 squares)
$\frac{1}{4}$ yellow (3 squares)    $\frac{1}{12}$ orange (1 square)

Key Lessons in Numeracy:
Numbers and the Number System Year 3

© P. Broadbent and K.Church 1999. Heinemann Educational Ltd.
For copyright restrictions, see reverse of title page.

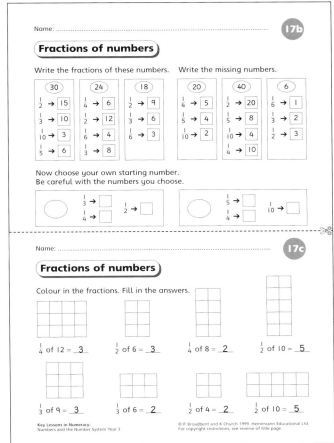

Name: .................................................

17b

**Fractions of numbers**

Write the fractions of these numbers.    Write the missing numbers.

30:
$\frac{1}{2}$ → 15
$\frac{1}{3}$ → 10
$\frac{1}{10}$ → 3
$\frac{1}{5}$ → 6

24:
$\frac{1}{4}$ → 6
$\frac{1}{2}$ → 12
$\frac{1}{6}$ → 4
$\frac{1}{3}$ → 8

18:
$\frac{1}{2}$ → 9
$\frac{1}{3}$ → 6
$\frac{1}{6}$ → 3

20:
$\frac{1}{4}$ → 5
$\frac{1}{5}$ → 4
$\frac{1}{10}$ → 2

40:
$\frac{1}{2}$ → 20
$\frac{1}{5}$ → 8
$\frac{1}{10}$ → 4

6:
$\frac{1}{6}$ → 1
$\frac{1}{3}$ → 2
$\frac{1}{2}$ → 3

Now choose your own starting number.
Be careful with the numbers you choose.

$\frac{1}{3}$ →    $\frac{1}{2}$ →
$\frac{1}{4}$ →

$\frac{1}{5}$ →    $\frac{1}{10}$ →
$\frac{1}{4}$ →

Name: .................................................

17c

**Fractions of numbers**

Colour in the fractions. Fill in the answers.

$\frac{1}{4}$ of 12 = _3_    $\frac{1}{2}$ of 6 = _3_    $\frac{1}{4}$ of 8 = _2_    $\frac{1}{2}$ of 10 = _5_

$\frac{1}{3}$ of 9 = _3_    $\frac{1}{3}$ of 6 = _2_    $\frac{1}{2}$ of 4 = _2_    $\frac{1}{2}$ of 10 = _5_

Key Lessons in Numeracy:
Numbers and the Number System Year 3

© P. Broadbent and K.Church 1999. Heinemann Educational Ltd.
For copyright restrictions, see reverse of title page.

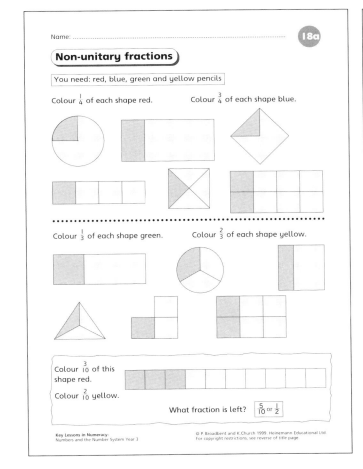

Name: .................................................

18a

**Non-unitary fractions**

You need: red, blue, green and yellow pencils

Colour $\frac{1}{4}$ of each shape red.    Colour $\frac{3}{4}$ of each shape blue.

Colour $\frac{1}{3}$ of each shape green.    Colour $\frac{2}{3}$ of each shape yellow.

Colour $\frac{3}{10}$ of this shape red.
Colour $\frac{2}{10}$ yellow.

What fraction is left? $\frac{5}{10}$ or $\frac{1}{2}$

Key Lessons in Numeracy:
Numbers and the Number System Year 3

© P. Broadbent and K.Church 1999. Heinemann Educational Ltd.
For copyright restrictions, see reverse of title page.

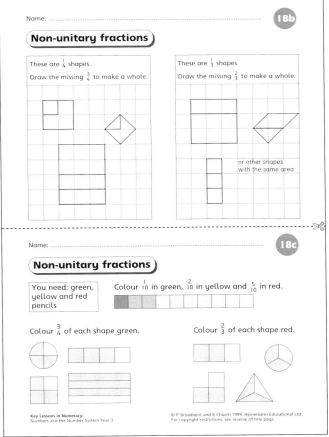

Name: .................................................

18b

**Non-unitary fractions**

These are $\frac{1}{4}$ shapes.
Draw the missing $\frac{3}{4}$ to make a whole.

These are $\frac{1}{3}$ shapes.
Draw the missing $\frac{2}{3}$ to make a whole.

or other shapes
with the same area

Name: .................................................

18c

**Non-unitary fractions**

You need: green, yellow and red pencils

Colour $\frac{1}{10}$ in green, $\frac{2}{10}$ in yellow and $\frac{5}{10}$ in red.

Colour $\frac{3}{4}$ of each shape green.    Colour $\frac{2}{3}$ of each shape red.

Key Lessons in Numeracy:
Numbers and the Number System Year 3

© P. Broadbent and K.Church 1999. Heinemann Educational Ltd.
For copyright restrictions, see reverse of title page.

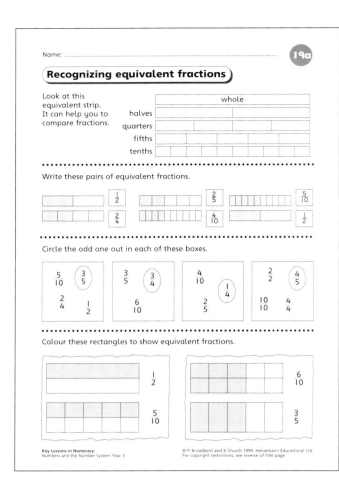

**Name:** ...........................................   19a

**Recognizing equivalent fractions**

Look at this equivalent strip. It can help you to compare fractions.

| | whole | |
|---|---|---|
| halves | | |
| quarters | | |
| fifths | | |
| tenths | | |

Write these pairs of equivalent fractions.

$\frac{1}{2}$   $\frac{2}{5}$   $\frac{5}{10}$

$\frac{2}{4}$   $\frac{4}{10}$   $\frac{1}{2}$

Circle the odd one out in each of these boxes.

$\frac{5}{10}$  ③⁄₅   $\frac{3}{5}$  ③⁄₄   $\frac{4}{10}$   $\frac{2}{2}$  ④⁄₅

$\frac{2}{4}$  $\frac{1}{2}$   $\frac{6}{10}$   ①⁄₄  $\frac{2}{5}$   $\frac{10}{10}$  $\frac{4}{4}$

Colour these rectangles to show equivalent fractions.

$\frac{1}{2}$   $\frac{6}{10}$

$\frac{5}{10}$   $\frac{3}{5}$

Key Lessons in Numeracy:
Numbers and the Number System Year 3
© P. Broadbent and K. Church 1999. Heinemann Educational Ltd
For copyright restrictions, see reverse of title page

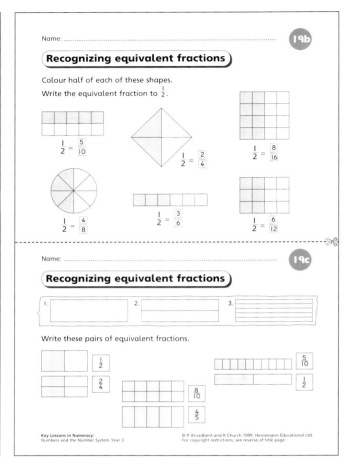

**Name:** ...........................................   19b

**Recognizing equivalent fractions**

Colour half of each of these shapes.
Write the equivalent fraction to $\frac{1}{2}$.

$\frac{1}{2} = \frac{5}{10}$   $\frac{1}{2} = \frac{2}{4}$   $\frac{1}{2} = \frac{8}{16}$

$\frac{1}{2} = \frac{4}{8}$   $\frac{1}{2} = \frac{3}{6}$   $\frac{1}{2} = \frac{6}{12}$

**Name:** ...........................................   19c

**Recognizing equivalent fractions**

1.    2.    3.

Write these pairs of equivalent fractions.

$\frac{1}{2}$   $\frac{5}{10}$

$\frac{2}{4}$   $\frac{8}{10}$   $\frac{1}{2}$

$\frac{4}{5}$

Key Lessons in Numeracy:
Numbers and the Number System Year 3
© P. Broadbent and K. Church 1999. Heinemann Educational Ltd
For copyright restrictions, see reverse of title page

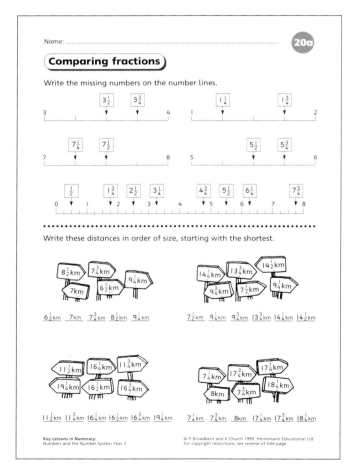

**Name:** ...........................................   20a

**Comparing fractions**

Write the missing numbers on the number lines.

$3\frac{1}{2}$   $3\frac{3}{4}$      $1\frac{1}{4}$   $1\frac{3}{4}$
3 ——————— 4    1 ——————— 2

$7\frac{1}{4}$   $7\frac{1}{2}$      $5\frac{1}{2}$   $5\frac{3}{4}$
7 ——————— 8    5 ——————— 6

$\frac{1}{2}$   $1\frac{3}{4}$  $2\frac{1}{2}$  $3\frac{1}{4}$   $4\frac{3}{4}$  $5\frac{1}{2}$  $6\frac{1}{4}$   $7\frac{3}{4}$
0 — 1 — 2 — 3 — 4 — 5 — 6 — 7 — 8

Write these distances in order of size, starting with the shortest.

$8\frac{1}{2}$km  $7\frac{3}{4}$km  $9\frac{1}{4}$km  $7$km  $6\frac{1}{2}$km

$6\frac{1}{2}$km  $7$km  $7\frac{3}{4}$km  $8\frac{1}{2}$km  $9\frac{1}{4}$km

$14\frac{1}{4}$km  $13\frac{3}{4}$km  $14\frac{1}{2}$km  $7\frac{1}{2}$km  $9\frac{1}{4}$km

$7\frac{1}{2}$km  $9\frac{1}{4}$km  $9\frac{3}{4}$km  $13\frac{3}{4}$km  $14\frac{1}{4}$km  $14\frac{1}{2}$km

$11\frac{1}{2}$km  $16\frac{1}{4}$km  $11\frac{1}{4}$km  $19\frac{1}{4}$km  $16\frac{1}{2}$km  $16\frac{3}{4}$km

$11\frac{1}{2}$km  $11\frac{1}{4}$km  $16\frac{1}{4}$km  $16\frac{1}{2}$km  $16\frac{3}{4}$km  $19\frac{1}{4}$km

$17\frac{1}{4}$km  $17\frac{3}{4}$km  $18\frac{1}{4}$km  $8$km  $7\frac{1}{4}$km

$7\frac{1}{4}$km  $7\frac{3}{4}$km  $8$km  $17\frac{1}{4}$km  $17\frac{3}{4}$km  $18\frac{1}{4}$km

Key Lessons in Numeracy:
Numbers and the Number System Year 3
© P. Broadbent and K. Church 1999. Heinemann Educational Ltd
For copyright restrictions, see reverse of title page

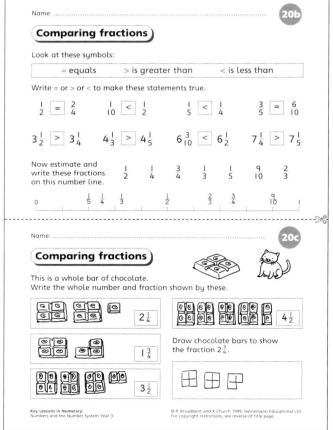

**Name:** ...........................................   20b

**Comparing fractions**

Look at these symbols:

| = equals | > is greater than | < is less than |
|---|---|---|

Write = or > or < to make these statements true.

$\frac{1}{2} = \frac{2}{4}$   $\frac{1}{10} < \frac{1}{2}$   $\frac{1}{5} < \frac{1}{4}$   $\frac{3}{5} = \frac{6}{10}$

$3\frac{1}{2} > 3\frac{1}{4}$   $4\frac{1}{3} > 4\frac{1}{5}$   $6\frac{3}{10} < 6\frac{1}{2}$   $7\frac{1}{4} > 7\frac{1}{5}$

Now estimate and write these fractions on this number line.

$\frac{1}{2}$   $\frac{1}{4}$   $\frac{3}{4}$   $\frac{1}{3}$   $\frac{1}{5}$   $\frac{9}{10}$   $\frac{2}{3}$

0 — $\frac{1}{5}$ $\frac{1}{4}$ — $\frac{1}{3}$ — $\frac{1}{2}$ — $\frac{2}{3}$ — $\frac{3}{4}$ — $\frac{9}{10}$ — 1

**Name:** ...........................................   20c

**Comparing fractions**

This is a whole bar of chocolate.
Write the whole number and fraction shown by these.

$2\frac{1}{4}$   $4\frac{1}{2}$

$1\frac{3}{4}$   Draw chocolate bars to show the fraction $2\frac{3}{4}$.

$3\frac{1}{2}$

Key Lessons in Numeracy:
Numbers and the Number System Year 3
© P. Broadbent and K. Church 1999. Heinemann Educational Ltd
For copyright restrictions, see reverse of title page